● CONTENTS

GRADE

UNIT 4 · WRITING
iting Explanations

UNIT 5 · GRAMMAR
Action Verbs

UNIT 6 · WRITING
Writing Letters

UNIT 7 · GRAMMAR
Linking Verbs

UNIT 8 · WRITING

Writing Stories

UNIT 9 · GRAMMAR

Adjectives

UNIT 10 · WRITING

Writing Descriptions

UNIT 11 · GRAMMAR

Pronouns

UNIT 12 · WRITING
Writing Persuasive Paragraphs

UNIT 13 · GRAMMAR
Adverbs

UNIT 14 · WRITING
Writing Research Reports

Name _____

What Is a Sentence?

> A **sentence** is a group of words that expresses a complete thought. A sentence tells about a person or thing and what the person or thing did.
>
> Most giant pandas come from China. = a sentence
> most giant pandas. = not a sentence

Read each group of words. If it is a sentence, write the word **sentence** on the next line. If it is not a sentence, add a word or words to make it a complete sentence. Write the complete sentence on the next line.

1. At birth, a giant panda is very small.

_____

2. Weighs only a few ounces.

_____

3. An adult can weigh up to 300 pounds.

_____

4. A big, round head and short, black ears.

_____

5. Eats mostly bamboo shoots and roots.

_____

6. A giant panda will eat some meat and fish.

_____

7. Saw two giant pandas at the San Diego Zoo.

_____

8. One giant panda.

_____

Macmillan Publishing Company

Extension: Have students write five sentences describing their favorite animals.

Declarative and Interrogative Sentences

> A **declarative sentence** is a sentence that makes a statement.
>
>   I went to first grade at Thompson Elementary School.
>
> An **interrogative sentence** is a sentence that asks something.
>
>   Where did you go to first grade?

A. If the sentence is a declarative sentence, write **D.** If it is an interrogative sentence, write **I.**

1. My first grade teacher was Mrs. Jenson. _____

2. Were you scared on your first day of school? _____

3. My sister walked to school with me. _____

4. First grade seems like such a long time ago now. _____

5. Which grade have you liked best? _____

6. My favorite so far has been fourth grade. _____

7. What do you want to do when you grow up? _____

8. I think I want to be a doctor. _____

B. Rewrite each sentence. Use a capital letter and the correct end punctuation.

9. is tomorrow Tim's birthday

   _____

10. tomorrow Tim will be nine years old

    _____

11. the weather will be warm and sunny

    _____

12. will the birthday party be held outside

    _____

Extension: Have students rewrite three declarative sentences in Part A to make them interrogative. Have them rewrite three interrogative sentences to make them declarative.

Name _____

Imperative and Exclamatory Sentences

> An **imperative sentence** is a sentence that tells or asks someone to do something.
>
> Throw the ball to Jack.
>
> An **exclamatory sentence** is a sentence that shows strong feeling.
>
> What a close game that was!

A. If the sentence is an imperative sentence, write **I.** If it is an exclamatory sentence, write **E.**

1. Come with me to the baseball tryouts. ____

2. Grab a bat from the dugout. ____

3. You hit the ball clear out of the park! ____

4. That was a powerful hit! ____

5. Try to hit a grounder the next time. ____

B. Rewrite each sentence. Use a capital letter and the correct end punctuation.

6. pitch a few balls to the coach

_____

7. what a terrific curve ball you just threw

_____

8. you're a great pitcher

_____

9. put on this team uniform

_____

10. play in this afternoon's game

_____

Extension: Have students write two imperative and two exclamatory sentences to tell about a sport they enjoy playing or watching.

Name

Complete Subjects and Complete Predicates

> The **complete subject** of a sentence includes all the words that tell whom or what the sentence is about.
>
>   <u>Huge dinosaurs</u> lived on the earth at one time.
>
> The **complete predicate** of a sentence includes all the words that tell what the subject does or is.
>
>   Some dinosaurs <u>walked on their hind legs</u>.

A. Draw one line under each complete subject. Draw two lines under each complete predicate.

1. Baby dinosaurs hatched from eggs.

2. Some dinosaurs flew through the air.

3. The sharp teeth of some dinosaurs chewed meat.

4. Many of these huge animals ate only plants.

5. Most scientists learn about dinosaurs from fossils.

B. Finish the following sentences about wild animals you can see today. Write either a complete subject or a complete predicate.

6. The monkeys in the tree _____

7. _____ licked its hurt paw.

8. The zebras _____

9. A huge grey elephant _____

10. _____ drank water from the lake.

11. Two giraffes _____

12. _____ showed her babies how to hunt.

13. The kangaroo _____

14. _____ scared us with his loud cry.

Extension: Ask students to select five sentences from a book and identify the complete subject and the complete predicate in each.

Name _____

Simple Subjects

> The **complete subject** includes all the words that tell whom or what the sentence is about.
>
>   A big circus came to town.
>
> The **simple subject** is the main word or group of words in the complete subject.
>
>   A big circus came to town.

A. Circle the complete subject. Then write the simple subject in each sentence.

1. A loud parade marched down Main Street.   _____

2. Three of my friends bought tickets quickly.   _____

3. A tall man announced the acts.   _____

4. Large lions performed amazing tricks.   _____

5. Six clowns popped out of a small car.   _____

6. A beautiful girl rode on the back of a horse.   _____

7. Very brave men walked across a high wire.   _____

8. Many elephants circled the ring three times.   _____

9. Five little dogs jumped through a hoop.   _____

10. The happy people clapped at the end.   _____

B. Complete each sentence by writing a simple subject.

11. After the circus, several _____ fed the animals.

12. The circus _____ put their horns, drums, and other instruments away.

13. The _____ walked to their trailers.

14. In the kitchen, _____ began to make dinner.

15. The _____ in the audience went to their homes.

Macmillan LANGUAGE ARTS TODAY
Grade 4, Unit 1, Lesson 5, pages 10–11

Extension: Have students work in pairs. Ask one student to write five sentences about the circus. Then ask the other student to underline the simple subject in each sentence. Finally, have students switch roles and repeat the activity.

Name _____

Simple Predicates

> The **complete predicate** includes all the words that tell what the subject does or is.
>
>   Volcanoes begin deep inside the earth.
>
> The **simple predicate** is the main word or group of words in the complete predicate.
>
>   Volcanoes begin deep inside the earth.

A. Circle the complete predicate. Then write the simple predicate.

1. A volcano looks like a mountain with fireworks. _____

2. Smoke pours out of the mountain's top. _____

3. Fire also shoots out of the top. _____

4. Then hot lava flows over the top. _____

5. The flaming rocks roll down the sides of
   the mountain. _____

6. Trees in the path of the lava burn completely. _____

7. The lava rushes toward the bottom. _____

8. People leave their homes. _____

9. Often, fire destroys whole towns. _____

10. Scientists study volcanoes. _____

B. Complete each sentence by writing a simple predicate.

11. Earthquakes also _____ a lot of damage.

12. The ground _____ during an earthquake.

13. Buildings _____ during an earthquake.

14. Big cracks and holes _____ in the earth.

15. Fires _____ buildings and homes.

Macmillan LANGUAGE ARTS TODAY
Grade 4, Unit 1, Lesson 6, pages 12–13

Macmillan Publishing Company

Extension: Ask students to write the subject part of a sentence on an index card or a sheet of paper. Have students exchange their cards or papers and write a predicate to make a complete sentence. Have them underline the simple predicate.

Name _____

Compound Subjects and Compound Predicates

> A **compound subject** is two or more simple subjects that have the same predicate. The simple subjects are joined by **and.**
>
> A pencil and pen were on the desk.
>
> A **compound predicate** is two or more simple predicates that have the same subject. The simple predicates are joined by **and.**
>
> The pencil rolled and fell off the desk.

A. Draw a line under each compound subject.
Circle each compound predicate.

1. Mike and Doug took their dog for a walk.

2. The boat tipped and rocked in the stormy ocean.

3. Peaches and pears filled the basket.

4. The campfire crackled and blazed for hours.

5. Saturdays and Sundays are my favorite days of the week.

6. The bride and groom walked happily down the aisle.

7. The frog jumped and hopped across Jed's room.

8. The crowd cheered and clapped for the winning team.

B. A simple subject or simple predicate is missing from each sentence. Write a subject or a predicate that makes sense.

9. Dad often cooks and _____ on weekends.

10. We unpacked and _____ after our long trip.

11. Dogs and _____ often fight.

12. Tomatoes and _____ go into spaghetti sauce.

13. I swim and _____ during warm weather.

14. The lazy cat yawned and _____ .

15. The rain and _____ spoiled our picnic.

Macmillan Publishing Company

Extension: Have students write **CS** for *compound subject* or **CP** for *compound predicate* beside each sentence in Part B.

Name

Correcting Run-on Sentences

> A **run-on sentence** contains two or more sentences that run together.
>
> The ostrich has the biggest egg in the world and the egg weighs over three pounds and it is about seven inches long.
>
> To fix a run-on sentence, break it into shorter sentences.
>
> The ostrich has the biggest egg in the world. The egg weighs over three pounds. It is about seven inches long.

Fix each run-on sentence by breaking it into shorter sentences. Write the new sentences. Add capital letters and periods where needed.

1. An ostrich cannot fly and it is big and heavy and its wings are short.

_____

_____

2. An ostrich egg is large and it is much larger than a chicken's egg and some snakes eat ostrich eggs.

_____

_____

3. Ostriches live in groups and they live in the desert and they also live in grassy plains.

_____

_____

4. An ostrich runs very fast and it can run faster than a person and it can run almost as fast as a horse.

_____

_____

Extension: Have students write three sentences about an animal. Then ask students to exchange their papers with their partners and check each other's writing for run-on sentences.

Macmillan Publishing Company

Name _____

Mechanics: Punctuating Sentences

Every sentence must begin with a **capital letter.**

A **declarative** sentence makes a statement or tells something. It ends with a period.

My school bought ten computers**.**

An **interrogative** sentence asks something. It ends with a question mark.

Does your school have computers**?**

An **exclamatory** sentence shows strong feelings. It ends with an exclamation point.

What an exciting computer game**!**

An **imperative** sentence tells or asks someone to do something. It ends with a period.

Teach me how to play the game**.**

Write the following sentences correctly. Add a capital letter and the correct end punctuation.

1. this is how you use the computer

_____

2. have you ever used a computer before

_____

3. turn on that button

_____

4. follow the directions on the screen

_____

5. you're doing great

_____

Macmillan Publishing Company

Extension: Have students work in pairs to look through magazines to find examples of declarative, interrogative, exclamatory, and imperative sentences. Have them copy an example of each.

Vocabulary Building:
Using Context Clues

> **Context clues** are the words that come before and after an unfamiliar word in a sentence. The context clues in the following sentence can help you understand the meaning of the word *oasis*.
>
> In the middle of the desert, people and animals can stop for a drink of water at an <u>oasis</u>.
>
> The words *desert* and *water* tell you that *oasis* means "a supply of water in the desert."

Write the meaning for each underlined word.

1. Many trees and plants grow in the <u>fertile</u> land around an oasis.

  rich   sandy   _____

2. The water supply in some oases is enough for the animals that are always in the desert as well as the <u>transient</u> animals who do not stay there long.

  intelligent   temporary   _____

3. Oases usually <u>occur</u> along rivers and streams that flow into deserts.

  take place   take time   _____

4. Some <u>visible</u> streams can be seen for miles.

  hidden   noticeable   _____

5. Water from rain and underground springs also helps to <u>nourish</u> plants so that they grow very large.

  feed   pick   _____

6. The size of some oases has been greatly <u>augmented</u> so that there is much more water.

  made larger   made smaller   _____

7. <u>Irrigation</u> through pipes has created oases in the middle of some deserts.

  the supplying of water   the drinking of water   _____

Extension: Have students find an example of an unfamiliar word and the context clues provided in their science or social studies books. Have them share their findings with the class.

Macmillan Publishing Company

Name _____

Grammar and Writing Connection: Combining Sentences

- Use the word **and** or **but** to connect two sentences. **And** means "in addition."

  | Sports are a good form of exercise. | Exercise is healthy. |

  Sports are a good form of exercise, **and** exercise is healthy.

- **But** shows a contrast.

  | Some people like restful sports. | Others like active sports. |

  Some people like restful sports, **but** others like active sports.

- Use a comma before the joining word in a sentence.

  Fishing is a restful sport, but swimming is an active sport.

Combine each pair of sentences. Use **and** or **but.**

1. Some sports are played by one person. Other sports are played by many people.

   _____

   _____

2. Tennis can be played by two people. Baseball must be played by many.

   _____

   _____

3. Baseball is a team sport. Each team has nine players.

   _____

   _____

4. The Olympic Games began in Greece. They included sports like running and throwing.

   _____

   _____

Macmillan LANGUAGE ARTS TODAY
Grade 4, Unit 1, Grammar and Writing Connection, pages 22–23

Macmillan Publishing Company

Extension: Have students write two related sentences and then use _and_ or _but_ to join them.

Name

Group Writing:
A Personal Narrative

- A **personal narrative** tells something about what has happened to the writer.
- A personal narrative should have an **interesting beginning sentence** which tells the **main idea.**
- A personal narrative also contains **detail sentences** which support, or say more about, the main idea.
- A personal narrative should be written in **time order,** or the order in which the events actually happened.

In each of the following narratives, underline the detail sentence that is **not** in correct time order.

1.   A Day at the Beach

   On Saturday, everyone in my family put on bathing suits, grabbed a towel, and jumped into the car. At the end of the day we ended up with the worst sunburns of our lives because we had forgotten to use suntan oil. At the beach, we played in the water and built a huge sand castle. Then we ate a wonderful lunch that Billy and Kate had made.

2.   Getting a Pet

   For months, I had been asking Mom and Dad if I could have a pet. Then one day Mrs. Humphrey came to our door with a tiny kitten. It needed a home. Mom and Dad gave me money to buy the kitten food, a litter box, and some cat toys. After much discussion, my parents agreed to let me keep the cat.

3.   The Time I Tried Painting

   One day I didn't have anything special to do. I decided to paint a picture. I found some oil paints, paper, and a few brushes in a drawer. I started to paint a tree. When I tried to erase my mistake with a piece of paper towel, the brown and green paint smeared all over the paper. On the paper, I squirted some green paint for leaves and brown paint for the bark, but it didn't look right. That's when I decided that I would rather swim.

Extension: Have students add a detail sentence to two of the three narratives on this page.

Macmillan Publishing Company

Name

Thinking and Writing:
Main Idea and Details

- A personal narrative has a **main idea.** It can be the beginning sentence. It tells what the narrative will be about.
- The other sentences in the narrative are **detail sentences.** They support the main idea, or tell more information about it.

My class went on a trip to the zoo. ⟵——— **main idea**

We saw many kinds of animals.
We even fed some of them.
We wrote stories about the animals when ⟵**details**
we came back to school.

A. Read the paragraph. Underline the main idea sentence. Draw a line through the detail sentence that does not support the main idea.

   My puppy Maggie is always getting into mischief. On Tuesday, she chewed my mom's bedroom slippers. On Wednesday, she dug up Mrs. Samson's marigolds. Mrs. Samson has a dog named Freckles. Yesterday was the worst mischief yet. Maggie grabbed the meat that Grandma planned to cook for our supper and ran away with it.

B. Plan a personal narrative of your own. Write about an interesting or fun place that you have been to. First, write the main idea of your narrative and three details you want to include. Then, write your narrative as a complete paragraph on another piece of paper.

main idea _____

detail _____

detail _____

detail _____

_____

_____

Macmillan Publishing Company

Extension: Have students read a short article from a magazine and identify the main idea sentence and three detail sentences in that article.

Proofreading: Step 4

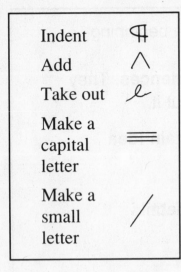

Indent	⊬
Add	∧
Take out	ℓ
Make a capital letter	=
Make a small letter	/

Read the paragraph about the pony express. See if there are any run-on sentences. Also, see if any sentences are missing end marks of punctuation.

A. Use the proofreading marks from the box to mark any errors you find. You can use the "Add" mark to show where punctuation marks should go.

In the mid-1800s, railroads only went to Missouri it was hard to get mail west to California The pony express system used horseback riders to carry the mail west what a long trip they had They hardly ever lost the mail, though imagine yourself as a pony express rider Would you have liked that job

B. Use the corrections and changes you marked to rewrite the paragraph on the lines below.

_____

_____

_____

_____

_____

_____

_____

_____

Name _____

Writer's Resources:
The Dictionary

Follow these steps to find a word in the dictionary:

1. Turn to the section of the dictionary that the word is in.

Beginning	Middle	End
a b c d e f g	h i j k l m n o p q	r s t u v w x y z

2. Find the correct page. Use **guide words** at the top of the page to help you. Guide words tell you the first and last words on a page.

lot/**low** ←— Guide words

lot	love
lotion	lovely
loud	low

3. Decide if the word falls between the guide words.

A. In what section of the dictionary would you find each of the following words? Write **beginning, middle,** or **end.**

1. crocodile _____   **6.** tadpole _____

2. wonderful _____   **7.** earth _____

3. stirrup _____   **8.** afraid _____

4. little _____   **9.** prize _____

5. mosquito _____   **10.** jellyfish _____

B. Circle all the words that come between each pair of guide words.

1. dangle/date		**2. separate/serious**		**3. plop/plump**	
dash	dawn	serve	serf	plow	plumber
data	danger	senses	series	plum	plus
day	dare	sequel	serve	plenty	plural

Extension: Have students find the following new words in a dictionary: *alligator, congress, nightingale, underpass,* and *vase.* Have students identify the guide words they used to find each new word.

Name _____

Writer's Resources: Dictionary Entries

A **dictionary entry** gives the following information about a word.
- the meaning or meanings of the word
- a sample sentence or sentences
- the number of syllables
- how to say the word
- how the word is used

---

galley (gal′ē) *n.* **1.** A large, low ship of long ago that had both sails and many oars. *Slaves or prisoners in chains usually rowed the oars in a galley.*
2. The kitchen of a ship. *Talk to the chef in the galley.*
gal · ley (gal′ē) *noun, plural* **galleys.**

A. Use the dictionary entry above for *galley* to answer the questions.

1. How many meanings are given for *galley*? _____

2. What sample sentence was given for the second meaning? _____

_____

3. How many syllables does the word *galley* have? _____

4. Is *galley* a noun or a verb? _____

5. How is the plural form of *galley* spelled? _____

B. Write a sentence using the first meaning of the word *galley*. Then write a sentence using the second meaning of the word *galley*.

6. _____

_____

7. _____

_____

Macmillan Publishing Company

Extension: Have students use a dictionary to find and then write two meanings for each of the following words: *bat, bark, duck,* and *fly.*

Name _____

What Is a Noun?

> A **noun** is a word that names a person, place, or thing.
>
> | **Person** | **Place** | **Thing** |
> |------------|-----------|-----------|
> | sister | school | table |

A. Write all the nouns in each sentence.

1. The people in my family cook. _____

2. My mom goes into the kitchen early. _____

3. Cereal tastes good in the morning. _____

4. My brother makes a large sandwich. _____

5. We eat fruit for dessert. _____

6. My dad makes hamburgers on the grill. _____

7. The fire is lit with a match. _____

8. Lettuce and tomatoes go into the salad. _____

9. The children usually drink milk. _____

10. The dog begs for scraps. _____

B. Write nouns that fit into each group listed at the top.

furniture	people	clothing	buildings
11. _____	_____	_____	_____
12. _____	_____	_____	_____
13. _____	_____	_____	_____
14. _____	_____	_____	_____
15. _____	_____	_____	_____
16. _____	_____	_____	_____

Macmillan Publishing Company

Extension: Have students list nouns that belong in the following categories: food, sports, occupations.

Name _____

Singular Nouns and Plural Nouns

A **singular noun** names only one person, place, or thing.
A **plural noun** names more than one person, place, or thing.
Add **s** to form the plural of most nouns.

    room   rooms   house   houses

Add **es** to form the plural of nouns ending in **s, x, ch,** or **sh.**

    boss   bosses   box   boxes
    match   matches   wish   wishes

A. Write the plural form of each noun.

1. church _____
2. room _____
3. pen _____
4. box _____
5. witch _____

6. class _____
7. ash _____
8. light _____
9. gas _____
10. dish _____

B. Write the plural form of each noun in parentheses.

11. Maria paints beautiful (picture) _____ of the country.

12. In one picture she painted two red (barn) _____ .

13. Look at the (bird) _____ in this picture.

14. You can almost hear them singing in the (branch) _____ .

15. There are green (plant) _____ growing in the shade.

16. Lovely (flower) _____ are growing in the sunny places.

17. Look closely at those (bush) _____ .

18. She painted two (fox) _____ looking out from behind them.

19. (Light) _____ are shining from the windows of the house.

20. If I had three (wish) _____ , one would be to live in a

peaceful place like the one Maria painted.

Extension: Have students write five sentences using each of the following words in plural form: *tax, fish, pitch, glass,* and *lamp.*

Name _____

More Singular Nouns and Plural Nouns

> A **singular noun** names only one person, place, or thing. A **plural noun** names more than one person, place, or thing. To form the plural of nouns ending with a vowel and **y**, add **s**.
>
>   play   plays   toy   toys
>
> To form the plural of nouns ending with a consonant and **y**, change the **y** to **i** and add **es**.
>
>   party   parties   fly   flies

A. Write the plural form of each noun.

1. lady _____
2. canary _____
3. story _____
4. donkey _____
5. worry _____

6. day _____
7. tray _____
8. factory _____
9. joy _____
10. valley _____

B. Write the plural form of each noun in parentheses.

11. _____ are my favorite times of the year.   (holiday)

12. There are always special things to eat like _____.
(cranberry)

13. For the Fourth of July, I save my _____ to buy flags.
(penny)

14. We go to different _____ to watch the fireworks.   (city)

15. Sometimes we take _____ to see relatives.   (journey)

16. I always love to see grandmother's _____.   (puppy)

17. Grandmother makes the most delicious _____.   (jelly)

18. At my uncle's house, we ride _____.   (pony)

19. There are always new _____ in the family to visit.   (baby)

Extension: Have students make a chart on their papers with the headings SINGULAR and PLURAL. Have them write each word below under the correct heading.
laundries   party   cherry   candies   countries   ray

Name _____

More Plural Nouns

Some plural nouns do not follow a regular spelling pattern. These nouns form the plural in a different way.

child ⟶ children   foot ⟶ feet   goose ⟶ geese

A few nouns have the same singular and plural forms.

deer   moose   salmon

A. Write the plural form of each noun.

1. mouse _____   6. man _____

2. sheep _____   7. tooth _____

3. woman _____   8. ox _____

4. trout _____   9. child _____

5. fish _____   10. scissors _____

B. Write the plural of each word. Then, write a sentence that uses each word.

11. man _____

_____

12. goose _____

_____

13. foot _____

_____

14. mouse _____

_____

15. women _____

_____

Extension: Have students use a dictionary to find the plural for each of these words: *life, loaf, calf, wolf.*

Name _____

Common Nouns and Proper Nouns

A **common noun** is a noun that names any person, place, or thing.

   teacher   state   building

A **proper noun** is a noun that names a particular person, place, or thing.

   Mr. Davis   Kentucky   Empire State Building

A. Underline each common noun. Draw a circle around each proper noun.

1. street
2. India
3. holiday
4. February

5. Mount Everest
6. Valentine's Day
7. month
8. mountain

9. Park Avenue
10. lake
11. country
12. Atlantic Ocean

B. Under each common noun, write a proper noun that could take its place.

13. girl

_____

14. planet

_____

15. school

_____

16. street

_____

17. lake

_____

18. teacher

_____

19. day

_____

20. language

_____

21. man

_____

22. state

_____

23. team

_____

24. ocean

_____

Extension: Have students work with a partner to list five common and five proper nouns.

Name _____

Singular Possessive Nouns

> A **possessive noun** shows who or what owns or has something. A singular noun that shows ownership is called a **singular possessive noun.**
>
> Add an apostrophe and **s** (**'s**) to form the possessive of a singular noun.
>
> boy boy's   bicycle bicycle's   door door's

A. Write the possessive form of each underlined noun.

1. the skates of my <u>brother</u>   my _____ skates

2. the blanket of the <u>baby</u>   the _____ blanket

3. the claws of the <u>bear</u>   the _____ claws

4. the whiskers of the <u>cat</u>   the _____ whiskers

5. the petals of the <u>rose</u>   the _____ petals

6. the name of the <u>girl</u>   the _____ name

7. the suitcase of the <u>man</u>   the _____ suitcase

8. the rays of the <u>sun</u>   the _____ rays

B. Write the correct possessive form of each singular noun in parentheses.

9. That (boy) _____ face looked familiar.

10. Was he Tim, the (doctor) _____ son?

11. No, her (son) _____ hair is curly.

12. The boy you saw works in the (school) _____ library.

13. He is the (librarian) _____ helper.

14. He repaired this (book) _____ cover.

15. He is my (brother) _____ age.

Extension: Have students use three of the phrases with possessive nouns in Part A in their own sentences.

Name

Plural Possessive Nouns

> A **possessive noun** is a noun that names who or what has something. A plural noun that shows ownership is a **plural possessive noun.**
>
> Add an apostrophe (') to form the possessive of plural nouns that end in **s.**
>
> chickens $'$ tulips $'$ barns $'$
>
> Add an apostrophe and **s** (**'s**) to form the possessive of plural nouns that do not end in **s.**
>
> men   men $'s$ mice   mice $'s$ children   children $'s$

A. Write the possessive form of each underlined noun.

1. the home of the <u>ants</u>   the _____ home

2. the tails of the <u>dogs</u>   the _____ tails

3. the horns of the <u>cars</u>   the _____ horns

4. the buses of the <u>children</u>   the _____ buses

5. the suits of the <u>women</u>   the _____ suits

6. the toys of my <u>sisters</u>   my _____ toys

7. the roots of the <u>plants</u>   the _____ roots

8. the feathers of the <u>geese</u>   the _____ feathers

B. Write the correct possessive form of each plural noun in parentheses.

9. The (players) _____ uniforms just arrived.

10. The (men) _____ shirts are too small.

11. The (boxes) _____ lids have been torn.

12. The (boys) _____ shorts are missing.

13. The (children) _____ hats are also missing.

14. We have lost 100 (dollars) _____ worth of uniforms.

Macmillan Publishing Company

Macmillan LANGUAGE ARTS TODAY
Grade 4, Unit 3, Lesson 7, pages 88–89

Extension: Have students write the plural possessive form of each of the following nouns: *flowers, sheep, cows, women, ducks, deer, bugs,* and *children.* Then, have students use three of these plural possessive nouns in sentences.

Name _____

Using Possessive Nouns

A **possessive noun** names who or what owns or has something.
Add an apostrophe and **s** (**'s**) to form the possessive of most
singular nouns.

girl's   car's   school's

Add an apostrophe (') to form the possessive of plural nouns that
end in **s**.

horses'   teachers'   cats'

Add an apostrophe and **s** (**'s**) to form the possessive of plural nouns
that do not end in **s**.

men's   geese's   children's

A. Read the nouns in the first column. Then underline the correct
possessive form of each noun.

1. **elephant**	elephant's	elephants'
2. **mice**	mice's	mices'
3. **mothers**	mothers's	mothers'
4. **babies**	babies's	babies'
5. **women**	women's	womens'
6. **farmer**	farmers'	farmer's
7. **astronaut**	astronaut's	astronauts'
8. **kitten**	kittens'	kitten's

B. Write the correct possessive form of each noun in parentheses.

9. Yesterday, the (sun) _____ bright light woke me.

10. I was awake before I heard my (brothers) _____ alarm.

11. However, I was moving at a (snail) _____ pace.

12. Then I heard my (sister) _____ voice calling me.

13. When I realized that my (mother) _____ special pancakes

were being served for breakfast, I quickly ran downstairs.

Extension: Have students choose one singular and one plural
possessive noun that they underlined in Part A to use in
sentences. Then have them exchange papers and draw an
illustration for each.

Macmillan Publishing Company

Name _____

Mechanics: Abbreviations

> An **abbreviation** is a short form of a word. Most abbreviations begin
> with a capital letter and end with a period.
>
> | Titles | Addresses | Days | Months |
> |---|---|---|---|
> | Dr./Doctor | St./Street | Fri./Friday | Feb./February |
> | Mr./Mister | Co./Company | Sat./Saturday | Dec./December |

A. Rewrite each of the following items. Use the abbreviation of the
word or words in parentheses.

1. (a woman) Sally Smith _____

2. 234 Evergreen (street) _____

3. (Saturday), (January) 23 _____

4. (doctor) Roger Thompson _____

5. (Mister) Richard Joseph _____

B. Rewrite each sentence. Use abbreviations wherever possible.

6. We will meet on the first Tuesday in September.

_____

7. We all signed the letter to Governor Anthony Spinelli.

_____

8. Mister Harry Rosen now lives on Emery Street.

_____

9. Last Monday, Doctor Maria Rodriguez moved to Portland.

_____

10. On Thursday, September 23, I wrote a letter to the Mason Company at
234 Keating Drive in New York.

_____

_____

Extension: Have students work in pairs. Give each pair two
index cards. Have them take turns writing and addressing a
"post card" to their partner. Have them use as many
abbreviations as possible.

Name _____

Vocabulary Building:
Compound Words

> A **compound word** is a word made by joining two or more short words together.
>
> week + end = weekend   mail + box = mailbox

Write the new word that is formed by combining the two words. Then use each word in a sentence.

1. birth + day = _____

_____

2. moon + light = _____

_____

3. air + plane = _____

_____

4. rain + coat = _____

_____

5. news + paper = _____

_____

6. shoe + lace = _____

_____

7. base + ball = _____

_____

8. bird + seed = _____

_____

9. finger + print = _____

_____

Extension: Have students use a dictionary to find six compound words. Then, have students choose three of the words to illustrate.

Name

Grammar and Writing Connection: Combining Sentences

You can show that ideas are linked when you use the joining word **and.**

SEPARATE: My brother Jason joined the track team. His friend Jeffrey joined the track team.

My brother Jason and his friend Jeffrey joined the track team.

You can show a choice between ideas when you use the joining word **or.**

SEPARATE: Jason will run the 100-meter race. Jason will run the relay race.

Jason will run the 100-meter race or the relay race.

Combine each pair of sentences. Use **and** or **or.**

1. Parents came to the track meet. Teachers came to the track meet.

2. Girls are on the track team. Boys are on the track team.

3. Is the relay race first? Is the broad jump first?

4. Judges are watching the runners. Judges are watching the finish line.

5. Did Jeffrey hurt his ankle? Did Jeffrey hurt his knee?

6. Jason came in second place. Jason came in third place.

7. The team members were excited. The team members were happy.

Extension: Have students write two pairs of sentences with similar ideas and combine them by using *and* or *or.*

Name _____

Group Writing:
An Explanation

> When you write an **explanation,** you give facts and information about a topic. The **topic sentence** states the main idea. Each **detail sentence** gives facts that support the main idea.
>
> Baking bread takes time. ←————————— **Topic Sentence**
> First you must mix the ingredients. Then
> you must let the dough rise. After a few
> hours the dough is ready to be baked. ←—— **Detail Sentences**

A. Read the paragraph. Then follow the directions.

Clouds come in many different sizes and shapes. Cirrus clouds look like soft, white feathers. They are formed very high in the sky. Stratus clouds cover the sky like a thick blanket. Sometimes they mean that rain is coming. Cumulus clouds are white, fluffy clouds. You see them mostly during good weather.

1. Write the topic sentence of this paragraph.

_____

2. Write three detail sentences that support the main idea.

1. _____

2. _____

3. _____

B. Read the paragraph. Then follow the directions.

By 1893, American life changed greatly because railroads finally connected all the corners of the United States. People living in one state could visit family and friends living in another state. Business improved because people were able to trade goods and products more easily. For example, fruits grown in California could easily be sent to New York. People could also leave the crowded cities and quickly travel to the country.

3. Circle the topic sentence. **4.** Underline each supporting detail sentence.

Extension: Have students add three detail sentences to this topic: There are many ways for people to travel.

Macmillan Publishing Company

Name _____

Thinking and Writing: Comparing and Contrasting

> Details that **compare** show how two things are alike.
>
>   An apple and a lemon are both fruits.
>
> Details that **contrast** show how two things are different.
>
>   An apple is larger than a lemon.
>   An apple is sweeter than a lemon.
>
> When you write a paragraph of comparison and contrast, you should include only those details that will support your topic.

Each of the writers named below is planning to write a paragraph of comparison and contrast. Help each one to think of details that support the paragraph's purpose. Write the missing details.

1. Leon's paragraph will compare skateboards and bicycles to show which one is better to have.

   Compare

   a. Both are fun.

   b. Both are a means of transportation.

   Contrast

   a. _____
   _____

   b. _____
   _____

2. Jamie's paragraph will compare baseball and football to give information about the two sports.

   Compare

   a. _____
   _____

   b. _____
   _____

   Contrast

   a. Football is a rougher sport.

   b. Baseball is easier to learn.

Extension: Have students find two pictures of a person, place, or thing in a magazine. Have them use details to compare and contrast the two pictures.

Proofreading: Step 4

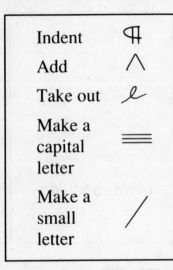

Indent	¶
Add	∧
Take out	ℓ
Make a capital letter	≡
Make a small letter	/

Read the following schedule of geography reports to be given by a fourth-grade class. Check to see if all plural nouns are spelled and used correctly. Also, make sure all nouns that name particular people or places are capitalized.

A. Mark any errors you find in the paragraph with proofreading marks from the box.

On Monday, Joel harris will report on three type of trees that grow

along the mississippi river. On tuesday, carmen Sanchez will talk

about several animal that live in the rocky Mountains. On wednesday,

Cassie benton will tell about some plant that grow in the Mojave

desert. On thursday, nori hirata will discuss three use of the energy

that comes from niagara falls. Finally, on friday, the childs will discuss

all the report.

B. Rewrite the schedule on the lines below. Make the corrections you marked above.

_____

_____

_____

_____

_____

_____

Macmillan Publishing Company

Name _____

Writer's Resources:
The Library

Library books are kept in three main sections.

- **Fiction** books contain made-up stories.
- **Nonfiction** books contain facts and practical information.
- **Reference** books also contain facts and practical information. Reference books include dictionaries, encyclopedias, and atlases.

A. In which part of the library would you find each book? Write **fiction, nonfiction,** or **reference.**

1. *Webster's Dictionary* _____

2. *How to Make a Graph* _____

3. *Collier's Encyclopedia* _____

4. *The Moon Mystery* _____

5. *Learning to Eat Right* _____

6. *Eddie the Dog Holder* _____

7. *The Bears on Hemlock Mountain* _____

8. *The World Atlas* _____

9. *Sign Language for the Young* _____

10. *Three Boys and a Tug Boat* _____

B. Circle the answer you choose to each question.

11. Which of these titles names a fiction book?

    a. *The Wizard of Oz*   b. *Webster's New Collegiate Dictionary*

12. Which of these books would be in the reference section?

    a. *Robin Hood*   b. *Collier's Encyclopedia*

13. Which of these books is a nonfiction book?

    a. *The Wind in the Willows*   b. *Restless Oceans*

Macmillan LANGUAGE ARTS TODAY
Grade 4, Unit 4, Lesson 5, pages 142–143

Extension: Have students categorize each book in the classroom library collection as either fiction, nonfiction, or reference.

Name

Writer's Resources:
The Card Catalog

The **card catalog** contains cards on all the books in the library.

- The **title card** shows the title first.
- The **author card** lists the author's last name first.
- The **subject card** begins with the subject of the book.
- The **call number** is in the upper left corner.

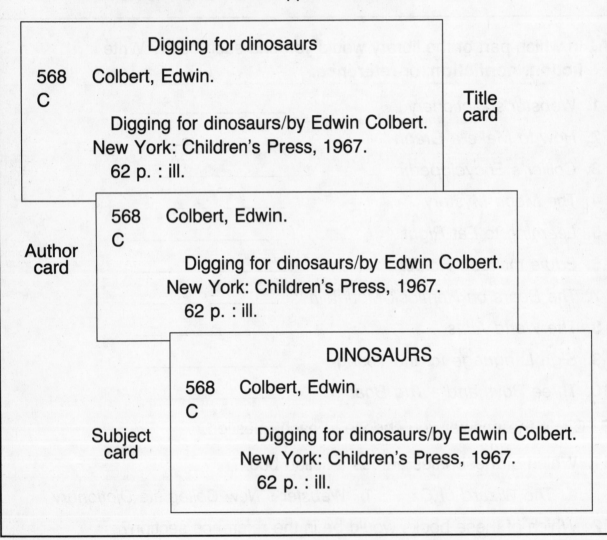

Use the catalog cards above to answer the following questions.

1. What is the title of this book? _____

2. Who wrote this book? _____

3. What is the call number of this book? _____

Extension: Have students work in pairs. Have each pair choose a book from the classroom library or have them bring a favorite book from home. Have them prepare a title, author, and subject card for each book.

Name

What Is an Action Verb?

> An **action verb** is a verb that expresses action. It tells what the subject does or did.
>
> Dan <u>scattered</u> the seeds over the soil.

A. Circle all the words that make sense in the blank. Those words are action verbs.

1. Every year, my family ____ a vegetable garden.

    plans   around   grows   begins   three

2. Mom always ____ tomato and lettuce seeds.

    top   buys   chooses   quickly   plants

3. Later, everyone ____ the growing young plants.

    waters   admires   through   tall   tasty

4. In July, we ____ our first fresh peas.

    dirt   pick   without   taste   cook

5. I always ____ salads with fresh vegetables.

    lunch   make   enjoy   bowl   eat

B. On the line, write an action verb that makes sense in the sentence.

6. We always _____ up front at the movies.

7. Karen _____ mysteries.

8. I _____ my eyes at the scary parts.

9. Karen _____ the entire movie.

10. First, the detectives _____ for clues.

11. Then, they always _____ the person they are after.

12. At the end, the detectives _____ the mystery.

Extension: Ask students to cut out action pictures from an old magazine. Have them paste the pictures on paper and write action verbs to make an action collage.

Name _____

Main Verbs and Helping Verbs

> The **main verb** is the most important verb in the sentence.
>   The airplane <u>lands</u> smoothly.
>
> A **helping verb** is a verb that comes before the main verb.
>   The airplane <u>will</u> land smoothly.

A. Draw a line under each helping verb. Circle each main verb.

1. We are leaving for the airport in ten minutes.

2. Danny is waiting for us in the station wagon.

3. Tommy was looking for our runaway dog.

4. Dad is talking on the telephone in his office.

5. Mom will finish her paper work in two minutes.

6. The airplane will arrive at six o'clock this evening.

7. My older brother is coming from California.

B. Write the helping verb and the main verb on the line.

8. My brother will stay with us for two weeks. _____

9. He was going to college in California. _____

10. He has taken many writing courses. _____

11. He will write for a newspaper one day. _____

12. He has studied very hard. _____

13. He was getting good grades. _____

14. He will become a famous writer. _____

15. Two of his stories were published already. _____

Extension: Have students write four sentences to describe a book they have read. Have them include a helping verb and main verb in each sentence.

Name _____

Verb Tenses

A verb in the **present tense** tells what happens now.

Laura <u>walks</u> to school.

A verb in the **past tense** tells what has already happened.

Laura <u>walked</u> to school yesterday.

A verb in the **future tense** tells what will happen in the future. Verbs in the future tense have the helping verb **will.**

Laura <u>will walk</u> to school tomorrow.

A. Draw a line under the verb in each sentence. Then write whether the verb is in the **present tense,** the **past tense,** or the **future tense.**

1. Usually I ride my bike to school. _____

2. I will tell you a story about a rainy day. _____

3. My bike skidded. _____

4. My books, my bicycle, and I landed in a puddle. _____

5. I will remember that day forever. _____

6. Now my bicycle stays at home on rainy days. _____

B. Choose the correct verb. Write it on the line.

7. (present tense) John _____ for a hobby.

   paints   painted   will paint

8. (present tense) John also _____ baseball cards.

   collects   collected   will collect

9. (past tense) He _____ 200 cards in five years.

   saves   saved   will save

10. (future tense) He _____ to his collection throughout his life.

    adds   added   will add

Extension: Have students find two examples of verbs in the present tense, past tense, and future tense in their social studies textbooks.

Name _____

More About Verb Tenses

- A verb in the **present tense** tells what happens now.
  The temperature usually <u>drops</u> in January.
- A verb in the **past tense** tells what happened in the past.
  Last year, the temperature <u>dropped</u> in January.
- A verb in the **future tense** tells what will happen in the future.
  You can be sure that the temperature <u>will drop</u> this January.
- To write about the future, use the special verb **will**.

A. Underline each verb. Then write if the verb is **present tense, past tense,** or **future tense**.

1. Snow fell heavily last week. _____

2. We will build a huge snowman. _____

3. I make good snow balls. _____

4. I rolled the snowman's head and body. _____

5. The next time, I will make the snowman bigger. _____

6. Tina helped me. _____

7. She lives next door. _____

8. She will be in sixth grade next year. _____

9. The snowman looks handsome. _____

B. Write the correct form of the verb in parentheses.

10. Yesterday, we _____ to the park. (walk, past tense)

11. The park always _____ beautiful. (look, present tense)

12. Children _____ many games there. (play, present tense)

13. Ken and I _____ a basketball game. (watch, past tense)

14. Tomorrow, we _____ to the park again. (go, future tense)

Extension: Have students use newspapers to find two examples of verbs used in the present tense, two examples of verbs used in the past tense, and two examples of verbs used in the future tense.

Macmillan Publishing Company

Name

Subject-Verb Agreement

The verb must **agree** with the subject of a sentence.

- If the subject of a sentence is a singular noun or **he, she,** or **it,** the verb must be singular.

  A beaver swims through the water.

- If the subject of a sentence is a plural noun or **I, we, you,** or **they,** the verb must be plural.

  Beavers swim with their back feet.

A. Underline the correct verb from the pair in parentheses.

1. The tail of a beaver (look, looks) like a canoe paddle.
2. It (help, helps) the beavers to steer through the water.
3. The beavers' strong teeth (chew, chews) down several trees.
4. The trees (block, blocks) off the river or stream.
5. Instantly, a pond (form, forms).
6. Then, the beavers (swim, swims) quickly along the shore.
7. They (hunt, hunts) for the right size sticks and rocks for their house.
8. Soon, a huge winter home (rise, rises) out of the pond.
9. No wonder people (feel, feels) that the beaver is a good builder.
10. I (think, thinks) beavers are amazing!

B. Write the correct present tense verb in parentheses.

11. We _____ beavers in our pond.   (see)

12. I _____ the baby beavers.   (like)

13. The beaver house _____ over six feet tall.   (measure)

14. That big beaver _____ busy.   (look)

15. He _____ the other beavers of danger.   (warn)

16. His tail _____ hard on top of the water.   (slap)

17. The noise _____ the other beavers of danger.   (tell)

18. They _____ inside their house.   (rush)

Extension: Have students write **S** above every singular subject and **P** above every plural subject in sentences 1-10.

Name _____

Using Irregular Verbs I

> You do not always add **ed** to form the past tense of verbs. Verbs that do not add **ed** to form the past tense are called **irregular verbs.**
>
> | Verb | Past | Past with *has, have,* or *had* |
> |------|------|-------------------------------|
> | come | came | has, have, or had come |
> | drive | drove | has, have, or had driven |
> | eat | ate | has, have, or had eaten |
> | give | gave | has, have, or had given |
> | go | went | has, have, or had gone |
> | ride | rode | has, have, or had ridden |
> | run | ran | has, have, or had run |
> | see | saw | has, have, or had seen |
> | write | wrote | has, have, or had written |

A. Write the verb in parentheses in the past tense.

1. Mom (drive) _____ me to school yesterday.

2. I (run) _____ to my classroom.

3. I (give) _____ my teacher my homework.

4. Everyone (go) _____ to the auditorium.

5. We (see) _____ a movie about good health.

B. Write the verb in parentheses in the past tense using **has** or **have.**

6. Dad had (give) _____ me money to see a movie.

7. I have (go) _____ to three movies so far.

8. My sister Karen has (see) _____ some movies with me.

9. During outdoor concerts, we have (eat) _____ on the grass.

10. I have (write) _____ Dad a thank-you note.

Extension: Have students rewrite the sentences in Part A so that the verbs are in the past tense with *has, have,* or *had.*

Macmillan Publishing Company

Using Irregular Verbs II

You do not always add **ed** to form the past tense of verbs. Verbs that do not add **ed** to form the past tense are called **irregular verbs**.

Verb	Past	Past with *has*, *have*, or *had*
bring	brought	has, have, or had brought
do	did	has, have, or had done
draw	drew	has, have, or had drawn
fly	flew	has, have, or had flown
grow	grew	has, have, or had grown
make	made	has, have, or had made
sing	sang	has, have, or had sung
swim	swam	has, have, or had swum
take	took	has, have, or had taken
throw	threw	has, have, or had thrown

A. Write the verb in parentheses in the past tense.

1. Yesterday, I (take) _____ care of my younger brother.

2. For a while, we (throw) _____ a ball back and forth.

3. Then we (swim) _____ in the pool.

4. After that, we (draw) _____ some pictures.

5. During all of these activities, I (grow) _____ very tired!

B. Write the verb in parentheses in the past tense with **has** or **have** or **had.**

6. I had (make) _____ many paper airplanes.

7. I have (fly) _____ them in my backyard.

8. My neighbors have (bring) _____ some back to me.

9. They had (do) _____ this only two or three times.

10. I have just (draw) _____ a better model.

Macmillan Publishing Company

Extension: Have students look through their readers to find five examples of sentences in the past tense.

Name _____

Spelling Verbs Correctly

To form the present tense of many verbs, add **s**.

To form the past tense of many verbs, add **ed**.

The spellings of some verbs change when **es** or **ed** is added.

> For verbs that end with a consonant and **y**, change the **y** to **i** and add **es** or **ed**.
>
>> hurry = hurries or hurried   worry = worries or worried
>
> For verbs that end with one vowel and one consonant, double the final consonant and add **ed**.
>
>> step = stepped   wrap = wrapped
>
> For verbs that end with **e**, drop the **e** and add **es** or **ed**.
>
>> move = moves or moved   change = changes or changed

Write the correct present-tense or past-tense form of each verb in parentheses.

1. Yesterday, Sue (shop) with her father.   past   _____

2. They (stop) at several stores.   past   _____

3. Sue (remove) all of the receipts.   past   _____

4. She (place) them in her wallet.   past   _____

5. Today, Sue's father (notice) that the one shirt is too big.   present   _____

6. He (worry) that he lost the receipt.   present   _____

7. Sue (hurry) into the room.   present   _____

8. She (smile) at her father.   present   _____

9. "I (slip) the receipts into my wallet," she said.   past   _____

10. "Thank you," her father said. "You just (save) me twelve dollars."   past   _____

Extension: Have students list all the verbs on this page under the following headings.
Present Tense   Past Tense

Macmillan Publishing Company

Name _____

Mechanics: Using the Comma

A **comma** , is used after each word in a series.

On sale were fishing rods, hooks, and camping equipment.

A **comma** is needed to set off a person's name when the person is being directly addressed.

Jerry , did you see the sale at Jake's Department Store?

A **comma** is used after the words **yes, no,** and **well.**

Yes , let's go!

The commas are missing from the following sentences. Rewrite the sentences, using commas where they are needed.

1. Leroy Peter and Lee might like to join us on our fishing trip.

_____

2. Jane Paula and Sandy will also come with us.

_____

3. David do you think that would be too many people?

_____

4. No five is a good number.

_____

5. Jerry should we take tents sleeping bags and blankets?

_____

6. Yes it might be very cold at night.

_____

7. David do you remember how we almost froze last year?

_____

8. Jackets sweaters and woolen socks just couldn't keep us warm enough.

Macmillan Publishing Company

Extension: Have students write sentences that illustrate each of the comma rules explained on this page.

Name

Vocabulary Building:
Prefixes

A **prefix** is a word part added to the beginning of a word. A prefix changes the meaning of the base word.

Prefix	Meaning	Example
dis	not, opposite of	disagree (not agree)
im	not, without	impatient (not patient)
in	not, without	incapable (not capable)
un	not, opposite of	unkind (not kind)
non	not, opposite of, without	nonprofit (not for profit)
mis	incorrectly	misprint (print incorrectly)
pre	before	prearrange (arrange before)
re	again, back	replace (place again)

On the small blank line, write the meaning of each word. (Use the prefix as a clue.) Then write a sentence for each word.

1. remake _____

_____

2. imperfect _____

_____

3. dishonest _____

_____

4. unwanted _____

_____

5. preheat _____

_____

6. nonstop _____

_____

Extension: Have students use the dictionary to find examples of words with prefixes listed on this page.

Name _____

Grammar and Writing Connection: Making Subjects and Verbs Agree

Subjects and verbs must agree in sentences. In sentences with helping verbs, the helping verb in each sentence must also agree with the subject. **Has, have,** and **had** are helping verbs.

- Use **has** with a singular subject.

  Donna has read many books.

- Use **have** with plural subjects and **I** and **you.**

  Those people have gone to the library.
  I have borrowed many books.

- Use **had** with singular or plural subjects.

  The boy had bought many books.
  The boys had shared the cost.

A. Underline the helping verb that correctly completes the sentence.

1. I (has, have) been to the library.
2. Mrs. Parks (has, have) worked in the library for many years.
3. She (have, has) shown me many interesting books.
4. One book (had, have) told about rubber.
5. Rubber (have, has) been used to make many things.
6. Dad knows people who (have, has) seen rubber trees.

B. Correct the error in each sentence. First, underline the incorrect helping verb. Then, write the correct helping verb.

7. People has carried the rubber to factories. _____

8. A woman have poured the rubber into pans. _____

9. She have watched it dry and thicken. _____

10. Then rollers has pressed it into thin sheets. _____

11. My friend have never seen this process. _____

12. We has also seen how factories make
    rubber from chemicals. _____

Extension: Have students write **S** for *singular* and **P** for *plural* above each subject in Part B.

Name _____

Group Writing: A Friendly Letter

> A **friendly letter** has five parts.
> - The **heading** includes your address and the date.
> - The **greeting** usually includes the word *dear* followed by the person to whom you are writing.
> - The **body** includes everything that you want to say.
> - The **closing** is usually a way to say "good-bye."
> - The **signature** is your name, written under the closing.

Some parts and punctuation are missing in the letter below. Read the letter. Then answer the questions.

346 Brimmer Road
Chicago, Il 60614 —— **Heading**

Dear Grandmother —— **Greeting**
I hope you had a very happy New Year! On the first of January I made two New Year's resolutions. I am going to make better grades in school. I am also going to help Mom more around the house. Did you make any New Year's resolutions? —— **Body**
Mom and I are going to visit you in February during my vacation from school. I miss you very much.

Love, —— **Closing**
Nicky —— **Signature**

1. What is missing from the heading? _____

   Think of one that makes sense and add it to the heading.

2. What punctuation mark is missing from the greeting? _____

   Put one where it belongs.

3. How does the body of the letter begin? _____

   _____

4. How many paragraphs are there in the body of the letter? _____

5. Which word in the letter is the closing? _____

Macmillan LANGUAGE ARTS TODAY
Grade 4, Unit 6, Lesson 1, pages 200–203

Extension: Have students write a friendly letter to a family member or a friend.

Macmillan Publishing Company

Name _____

Thinking and Writing:
Solving Problems

To **solve a problem,** use a plan that includes the following steps.

- State what the problem is.
- State a possible solution.
- List the steps to follow to solve the problem.

Problem	Solution	Steps to Follow
What to make for an art project	Get ideas from a book.	1. Go to the library. 2. Find art books. 3. Look through the books for art project ideas.

Write a possible solution for each of the following problems. Then write the steps you would follow to reach that solution.

1. **Problem:** How to stay healthy in the winter

   Solution: _____

   Steps: _____

   _____

   _____

   _____

2. **Problem:** What to give a friend for her birthday

   Solution: _____

   Steps: _____

   _____

   _____

   _____

Macmillan Publishing Company

Extension: Have students work in groups to think of a problem they want to solve. Then have them think of a possible solution and the steps they should follow to reach that solution.

Name

Proofreading: Step 4

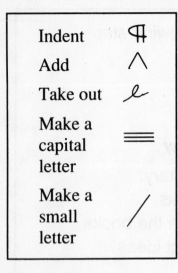

Indent	¶
Add	∧
Take out	ℓ
Make a capital letter	═
Make a small letter	/

Read this letter from a girl to her new pen pal. Make sure all the verb tenses are correct. Also, make sure commas are used where needed.

A. Use the proofreading marks from the box to mark errors in the letter. You may use the "Add" mark to show where commas should go.

December 3 1990

Dear Nicole

I get your first letter yesterday. I show it to my friend Amy. She will like you already. Your friends will sound like some of mine. You school sound like mine too. We were a lot alike. Please told me more about yourself. I tell you more about me too. Please will write again soon.

Your pen pal

Cheryl

B. Rewrite the letter. Include the corrections you marked above.

_____

_____

_____

_____

_____

_____

_____

Macmillan Publishing Company

Name _____

Writer's Resources:
Parts of a Book

> Knowing the parts of a book can help you find information.
>
> The **title page** is the first page of the book. It tells the title, the author, and the publisher of the book.
>
> The **copyright page** is after the title page. It tells the date the book was published.
>
> The **table of contents** lists the chapters and page numbers.
>
> The **body** of a book is the main part of the book.
>
> The **glossary** defines special words used in the book.
>
> The **index** lists topics alphabetically and page numbers where those topics can be found in the book.

Title Page	Glossary	Index
Learning About Science by Marvin Mays Warren Publishers, Inc. New York, New York	**barnacles** Small sea animals that attach themselves to objects. **barometer** An instrument used to measure air pressure.	Crabs......................228 Craters.....................271 Crust.......................116 Currents ....85 Cuttlefish.....................3

Use the title page, glossary, and index to answer each question.

1. What is the title of this book? _____

2. On what page would you find information about currents in the ocean? _____

3. What is the definition of *barometer*? _____

_____

4. Who is the publisher of the book? _____

5. On what page would you find information about craters? _____

6. Who wrote the book? _____

7. On what page would you find information about the earth's crust? _____

Macmillan Publishing Company

Extension: Have students locate each of the parts of a book explained on this page in one or more of their textbooks.

Name _____

What Is a Linking Verb?

> An **action verb** tells what the subject does or did.
>
>   Ken feeds the koalas every day.
>
> A **linking verb** links the subject of a sentence to a noun or adjective in the predicate. A linking verb does not express action.
>
>   Ken is a good zoo keeper. Ken is caring.

A. Write whether the underlined verb is an **action verb** or a **linking verb**.

1. Koalas are gentle animals. _____

2. People call koalas bears. _____

3. Koalas are really relatives of the kangaroo. _____

4. Koalas carry their babies in a pouch. _____

5. A baby koala is very small. _____

6. At six months, the baby leaves the pouch. _____

7. Koalas are interesting animals. _____

B. Draw a line under each linking verb. On the blank line, write the word in the predicate of the sentence that is linked to the subject.

8. The home of koala bears is Australia. _____

9. Leaves from certain trees are their main food. _____

10. A koala is a gentle animal. _____

11. The eyes of a koala are black. _____

12. Its nose is shiny. _____

13. Its ears are bushy. _____

12. It is tailless. _____

15. I am interested in koalas. _____

Extension: Have students write riddles using linking verbs and action verbs such as:

It is yellow at first.
Then it gets white.
It jumps when it gets hot. (popcorn)

Name _____

Linking Verbs in the Present Tense

Use **am** for the present tense when the subject is **I**.

    I am a fourth grader.

Use **is** for the present tense when the subject is **he, she, it,** or a singular noun.

    She is my best friend.   Kathy is my new neighbor.

Use **are** for the present tense when the subject is **you, we, they,** or a plural noun.

    We are neighbors.   Our homes are very nice.

Use **are** for the present tense when the subject is compound.

    Mom and Dad are farmers.

A. Circle the correct linking verb in each sentence.

1. The crow of a rooster (is, are) loud.

2. Betty and Sue (is, are) usually the first ones up in the morning.

3. You (is, are) the first one up this morning.

4. I (is, am) warm under the flannel covers.

5. My younger brothers (is, are) noisy.

6. They (is, are) very hungry in the morning.

B. Complete each sentence. Write the correct present tense linking verb.

7. Ducks _____ excellent swimmers.

8. Their webbed feet _____ cute.

9. A duck's beak _____ flat.

10. It _____ longer than a chicken's beak.

11. A duck and a goose _____ members of the same family.

12. I _____ a friend of the ducks.

Macmillan LANGUAGE ARTS TODAY
Grade 4, Unit 7, Lesson 2, pages 226–227

Extension: Have students write each simple subject in Part A.

Name _____

Linking Verbs in the Past Tense

Use **was** for the past tense when the subject is **I, he, she, it,** or a singular noun.

> She <u>was</u> a clown.   The show <u>was</u> wonderful.

Use **were** for the past tense when the simple subject is **you, we, they,** or a plural noun.

> You <u>were</u> great.   The people <u>were</u> amazed.

Use **were** for the past tense when the subject is a compound.

> Terry and Vicky <u>were</u> happy.

A. Circle the correct linking verb in each sentence.

1. Harry Houdini (was, were) a famous magician.

2. His real name (was, were) Ehrich Weiss.

3. He and his parents (was, were) immigrants.

4. Harry Houdini (was, were) very smart.

5. His magic tricks (was, were) amazing.

6. Houdini (was, were) best known for his escape tricks.

B. Complete each sentence with **was** or **were**.

7. Two years ago, David _____ a beginning magician.

8. His shows _____ always on Saturdays.

9. He _____ very clever.

10. A cloth and a ball _____ the props for one trick.

11. His friends _____ surprised at his talent.

12. I _____ happy to see his success.

13. His neighbors _____ happy, too.

14. They _____ big fans.

Macmillan Publishing Company

Extension: Have students underline the simple subject in each sentence on this page.

Using Linking Verbs

> **Am, is,** and **are** are present tense linking verbs. **Was** and **were** are past tense linking verbs.

A. Write the correct linking verb on the line.

1. Virginia and Lisa _____ sisters.   (is, are)

2. They _____ both good swimmers.   (is, are)

3. I _____ not a good swimmer.   (were, was)

4. Last summer, Lisa _____ my swimming teacher.
   (was, were)

5. I _____ a fast learner.   (am, is)

6. Today, we _____ all good swimmers.   (is, are)

7. Our summers _____ fun times at the pool.   (is, are)

B. Complete each sentence. Write the correct linking verb.

8. (present tense) _____ you a good swimmer?

9. (present tense) Swimming lessons _____ helpful.

10. (past tense) I _____ not a good swimmer before
    my lessons.

11. (past tense) My friends _____ worried about my safety.

12. (past tense) My mother and father _____ also worried.

13. (present tense) Today, they _____ proud of me.

14. (present tense) Finally, I _____ an expert.

15. (present tense) Now I _____ ready to be a swimming
    teacher.

16. (present tense) My students _____ learning how to be
    good swimmers.

Extension: Have students begin a story by saying a sentence that includes the linking verb *am, is, are, was,* or *were.* Then have other students add sentences to the story that also includes one of these linking verbs. Have them finish the story.

Name _____

Contractions with *not*

A **contraction** is a shortened form of two words. An **apostrophe** (') takes the place of one or more letters that are left out.

is not	= isn't	was not	= wasn't
are not	= aren't	were not	= weren't
has not	= hasn't	do not	= don't
have not	= haven't	could not	= couldn't

A. Draw a line under the contraction in each sentence. Then write the two words that make up the contraction.

1. I don't watch much television anymore.   _____

2. The shows haven't been very interesting lately.   _____

3. I couldn't find one good show last night.   _____

4. When the shows aren't interesting, I read.   _____

5. Isn't reading a good book a good idea?   _____

B. Write the contraction for each pair of words. Then write a sentence or a question that uses each contraction.

6. has not _____

_____

7. are not _____

_____

8. do not _____

_____

9. was not _____

_____

10. could not _____

_____

Extension: Have students write a list of as many contractions as they can think of in five minutes. Then have them work with a partner to combine their lists. The pair with the most contractions "wins"!

Macmillan Publishing Company

Name _____

Mechanics: Using Quotation Marks

- Use quotation marks to show a speaker's exact words.

    "Children often know more about computers than their parents do," said Uncle Steve.

- Never use quotation marks around words that tell who is speaking.

    "I like computers," he added.

- Do not use quotation marks when you do not use the speaker's exact words.

    Eileen said that she liked computers, too.

Rewrite each sentence. Add quotation marks where they belong.

1. I wish I had more time to learn about computers, said Dad.

_____

2. They really interest me, he added.

_____

3. Why didn't you learn about them at school? asked Eileen.

_____

4. Dad replied, They weren't there to learn about!

_____

5. What do you mean by that? asked Paul.

_____

6. When I was young, computers were big and expensive, Dad explained.

_____

7. Uncle Steve added, Most of us had never even seen one!

_____

8. The only place I saw them was in science–fiction movies, laughed Dad.

Extension: Have students write a short conversation between two people. Have them use quotation marks in the correct places.

Name

Vocabulary Building:
Suffixes

A **suffix** is a word part that is added to the end of a base word. A suffix changes the meaning of the base word to which it is added.

Suffix	Meaning	Example
able, ible	capable of, liable to	washable (capable of being washed)
er, or	one who does, that which does	teacher (one who teaches)
ful	full of	careful (full of care)
less	without	painless (without pain)
ly	in the manner of	quickly (in a quick manner)
ment	result	disappointment (result of being disappointed)
y	having, being like	dirty (having dirt)

A. Write the meaning of each word. Use the suffix as a clue.

1. useful _____

2. acceptable _____

3. painter _____

4. powerless _____

5. development _____

6. rainy _____

7. politely _____

8. flexible _____

9. calculator _____

10. cloudless _____

B. Choose five of the suffixed words above. Write a sentence for each one. Use another sheet of paper.

Extension: Ask students to use a dictionary to find words that have the suffixes listed on this page.

Name _____

Grammar and Writing Connection:
Combining Sentences

Sometimes sentences have related ideas. When ideas in separate
sentences are related, you can join them to make one sentence.
Use the word **and** or **but** to join related ideas.

SEPARATE: The students planned a show.
            They presented a show.

JOINED: The students planned and presented a show.

Combine each pair of sentences below.

1. Mom made some costumes. She gave them to the students.

_____

2. Jeff set up the lights. He didn't work them.

_____

3. Marie made programs. She gave them to the guests.

_____

4. Otis played the piano. He sang a song.

_____

5. Peter juggled some balls. He didn't juggle any hoops.

_____

6. Carey told some funny jokes. She made funny faces.

_____

7. Lynn pulled scarves out of a hat. She did some card tricks.

_____

8. The actors stood in front of the curtain. They waved to us.

_____

9. We clapped our hands. We cheered.

_____

Extension: Have students write two or more pairs of
sentences describing the variety show. Have students
combine the sentences using *and* or *but*.

Macmillan Publishing Company

PRACTICE·56

Group Writing: A Story

> A story should have:
>
> - interesting **characters** and **setting**.
>   The **characters** are the people in the story.
>   The **main character** is the most important character.
>   The **setting** is where and when the story takes place.
> - a good **beginning, middle,** and **end.**
>   The **beginning** introduces the characters, setting, and the plot.
>   The **middle** tells about the plot and the main character.
>   The **end** tells how the problem is solved.

A. Underline the answer to each question.

1. Which would not be a character in a story?
a. a dog named Ladd   b. a spaceship captain   c. a city in Ohio

2. Which would not be a setting?
a. a farmhouse   b. a mouse   c. a spaceship

3. What is a possible problem for a story?
a. A farmer raises corn and wheat.
b. A man loses his keys and is locked out of his car.
c. The mission of a spaceship is to explore Mars.

4. On its way to Mars, a spaceship gets lost. The directional equipment stops working. Which is not a way to solve the problem?
a. The space crew tries to radio to Earth for help.
b. The ship drifts in space forever.
c. The space crew tries to repair the directional equipment.

5. Which answer is one way the story about the spaceship might end?
a. While the spaceship wanders through space, it discovers a new planet.
b. The people in the spaceship pass the time by playing card games.
c. The captain of the spaceship tells everyone to take a week's vacation until the problem is solved.

Extension: Have each student identify the setting, main character, and other characters in his or her favorite story.

Macmillan Publishing Company

Name _____

Thinking and Writing:
Understanding Sequence

> A story's sequence of events must move logically from the beginning through the middle to the end. Events in a story are usually arranged in time order.

Two writers are planning stories. Right now, the main events in their plots are not in logical order. Number the events in the correct sequence, or the most logical order.

A. _____ Laurie Masters sprains her ankle toward the end of the race.

_____ She hobbles to the finish line and comes in third.

_____ She begins running after reading a story about a runner.

_____ The story of Laurie's courage is written in the school newspaper.

_____ She passes her best friend in the middle of the race.

_____ Laurie enters a school race.

_____ Laurie finds a book about famous athletes at the library.

B. _____ Ellis Jenkins makes two pitchers of lemonade.

_____ He buys lemons and paper cups.

_____ He decides to have a lemonade stand.

_____ Ellis thinks of another way to earn money.

_____ He sells only one glass of lemonade all day.

_____ Ellis wants to earn money during his summer vacation.

Extension: Have students choose a short story from their reader and list the story's setting and main characters. Then have them choose three important events from the story and illustrate them in time order.

Proofreading: Step 4

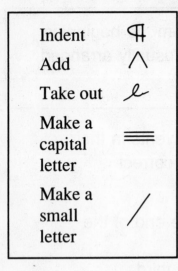

Indent	⸿
Add	∧
Take out	ℓ
Make a capital letter	=
Make a small letter	/

Read this conversation between some fourth-grade pupils on a class hike. Check to see whether all the verbs that link the subject with a word in the predicate are used correctly. Also see if quotation marks are used wherever they are needed.

A. Use the proofreading marks to mark any changes or corrections you want to make in the conversation.

"I are tired, moaned Justin.

"The rest area are just ahead, answered Mr. Parker.

This trail will be very long, puffed Mimi.

My feet is numb," complained Greg.

"My favorite activity now be reading, said Amy.

The next time, our hike is much shorter, promised Mr. Parker.

B. Write the conversation on the lines below. Make the changes and corrections you marked above.

_____

_____

_____

_____

_____

_____

_____

_____

Name _____

Writer's Resources:
The Thesaurus

A **thesaurus** is a reference book of synonyms and antonyms.
Synonyms are words that have the same or almost the same meaning.
Antonyms are words that have an opposite meaning. The following is a sample entry from a thesaurus.

> **TAKE**—(v.) catch, capture, get, receive, steal, swipe
> Antonyms—give, donate, offer

The word *take* in the sentence below may be replaced by a synonym for that word from the thesaurus entry.

Take the book from the shelf. Get the book from the shelf.

A. Use the thesaurus entry to answer the questions.

1. What part of speech is the word *take*?_____

2. Complete this sentence with the best synonym for *take.* At the end of the movie, the army will _____ the village.

3. What is an antonym for the word *take*?_____

4. Complete this sentence with the best antonym for *take.*

   We will _____ our old furniture to the Salvation Army.

B. Write a sentence or a question that uses each of the following synonyms for *take.*

5. **catch** _____

6. **get** _____

7. **steal** _____

8. **swipe** _____

9. **capture** _____

Extension: Have students use a thesaurus to find a synonym and an antonym for each of the following words: *joy, anger, fear,* and *pride.*

Name _____

What Is an Adjective?

> **Adjectives** are words that describe nouns. They can tell **what kind** or **how many,** and they usually come before the nouns they describe.
>
> A black dog is sleeping under our wooden porch.

A. Circle all the adjectives that describe each underlined noun.

1. This is a ____ <u>neighborhood</u>.

   work   quiet   pretty   without   friendly

2. We live in that ____ <u>house</u>.

   together   small   white   answer   corner

3. A ____ <u>friend</u> of mine lives in that apartment house.

   new   proudly   good   special   never

4. My grandfather planted that tree ____ <u>years</u> ago.

   inside   many   fifty   into   come

5. Every spring ____ <u>tulips</u> bloom in front of our house.

   colorful   went   red   many   through

B. Underline the adjective in each sentence. Write the noun the adjective describes.

6. I don't like cold weather. _____

7. I need a new coat. _____

8. My blue coat has a hole in it. _____

9. I must wear two sweaters under it. _____

10. Who lit the warm fire? _____

11. Our big dog always sits near the fire. _____

12. Our dog and cat are great friends. _____

Macmillan LANGUAGE ARTS TODAY
Grade 4, Unit 9, Lesson 1, pages 292–293

Macmillan Publishing Company

Extension: Have students write a description of a person, place, or thing in their classroom using as many adjectives as possible. Have the students read their descriptions to the class to see if they can guess what is being described.

Name _____

Adjectives After Linking Verbs

> Sometimes an **adjective** follows the noun it describes. When an adjective follows the noun it describes, the noun and adjective are connected by a linking verb.
>
> The sky was dark.

A. Write the adjective that describes each underlined noun.

1. Hurricane <u>watchers</u> are alert.   _____

2. <u>Equipment</u> for finding hurricanes is helpful.   _____

3. A hurricane's <u>wind</u> is powerful.   _____

4. A <u>hurricane</u> is very dangerous.   _____

5. During a hurricane, ocean <u>waves</u> are huge.   _____

B. Complete each sentence with an adjective that makes sense. You may wish to use the adjectives in the box.

high	dark	great	heavy	destructive
muddy	hurt	wet	dry	strong

6. Those clouds are quite _____.

7. The rain is very _____.

8. The winds are especially _____.

9. The last storm was _____.

10. At the end of the storm, the river was very _____.

11. The damage to our house was _____.

12. The basement was _____.

13. The walls were _____.

14. Luckily, no one was _____.

15. Finally, our house is _____ again.

Macmillan Publishing Company

Extension: Have students work in pairs to make a weather chart describing the weather at different points during the day. Have them use as many adjectives as possible. Have them display their charts to the class.

Name _____

Adjectives That Compare

> Add **er** to an adjective to compare two nouns.
>
> My dog is <u>bigger</u> than your dog.
>
> Add **est** to an adjective to compare more than two nouns.
>
> In fact, my dog is the <u>biggest</u> dog on this block.

A. Circle the correct form of the adjective in parentheses.

1. My dog Mutts is the (nicer, nicest) pet in the world.

2. Mutts is the (older, oldest) dog in the neighborhood.

3. He is much (friendlier, friendliest) than the neighbor's dog, King.

4. He is also (larger, largest) than King.

5. However, Mutts is (cuter, cutest) than King.

B. Write the correct form of the adjective in parentheses.

6. The first half of the talent show was (funnier, funniest) than the second half.   _____

7. The dancers' costumes were (prettier, prettiest) than the singers' costumes.   _____

8. Vince was the (louder, loudest) singer on the stage all evening.   _____

9. The (higher, highest) note was hit by Carrie during her song.   _____

10. During the tumbling act, Ted looked (stronger, strongest) than Rico.   _____

11. The dog act was (funnier, funniest) than the magician's act.   _____

12. The (shorter, shortest) act of the whole evening was Carmen's tap dance.   _____

Extension: Have students write sentences using the adjectives they did not circle in Part A.

Name

Spelling Adjectives That Compare

When adding **er** or **est** to adjectives, follow these spelling rules.

If a one-syllable adjective ends with a consonant-vowel-consonant, double the final consonant before adding **er** or **est**.

    flat   **flatter**   **flattest**

If an adjective ends with **e**, drop the **e** before adding **er** or **est**.

    safe   **safer**   **safest**

If an adjective ends with a consonant and **y**, change the **y** to **i** and add **er** or **est**.

    happy   **happier**   **happiest**

Write the correct **er** or **est** form of the adjective in parentheses.

1. The weather is (warm) _____ today than it was yesterday.

2. Even the sun seems (bright) _____ than it was yesterday.

3. In fact, this might be the (hot) _____ day of the year.

4. It is hot in the summer because the sun's rays are (close) _____ to the earth than during the winter.

5. The (late) _____ setting of the sun so far has been 8:30 P.M.

6. I am (happy) _____ in the summer than I am in the winter.

7. To me, the (lovely) _____ temperature of all is 90 degrees.

8. At 90 degrees I feel (lively) _____ than I do at 60 degrees.

9. I wear my (light) _____ clothes in the summer.

10. I think summer is the (pretty) _____ season of the year.

11. Sometimes I'm (lazy) _____ on a summer day than I would be on a fall day.

12. I think that people are (friendly) _____ in the summer than they are in the winter.

Extension: Have students write the *er* and *est* forms of these words: *soft, sorry, red, smooth,* and *large.*

Name

Comparing with *more* and *most*

Use **more** and **most** with most adjectives that have two or more syllables. Use **more** to compare two nouns.

Jeff is <u>more</u> cheerful than Bob.

Use **most** to compare more than two nouns.

Jeff is the <u>most</u> cheerful student in the fourth grade.

Never use **more** or **most** with an adjective that already has an **er** or **est** ending.

Incorrect: The last joke was the most funniest of all.
Correct: The last joke was the funniest of all.

A. Circle the correct form of the adjective in parentheses.

1. Jeff is the (more active, most active) student in the fourth grade.

2. He is also the (more funny, most funny) person I know.

3. Mark is (more serious, most serious) than Jeff.

4. To Jeff, swimming is (more enjoyable, most enjoyable) than watching TV.

5. The swim meet on Saturday will be his (more important,

most important) race.

B. Complete each sentence with the adjective in parentheses and
more or **most.**

6. I think swimming is (difficult) _____ to learn than

riding a bicycle.

7. I am (excited) _____ about swimming than I was

six months ago.

8. Now my arms and legs are the (powerful) _____

parts of my body.

Extension: Have students choose two or three items in the classroom that they can compare in oral sentences using the words *more* and *most.*

Macmillan Publishing Company

Name _____

Using Articles

> The words **a, an,** and **the** are special adjectives called **articles.** Use **an** before a singular noun that begins with a vowel. Use **a** before a singular noun that begins with a consonant.
>
>   <u>an</u> egg   <u>a</u> fish
>
> The article **the** is used before a singular noun that names a particular person, place, or thing and before all plural nouns.
>
>   <u>the</u> man   <u>the</u> men

A. Draw a line under each article. Write the noun each article points out.

1. Look at the helicopter.   _____

2. It will land on top of the building.   _____

3. Most planes need an airport.   _____

4. A helicopter doesn't even need a runway.   _____

5. There are many uses for a helicopter.   _____

B. Complete each sentence by writing the correct article.

6. Long ago, people sometimes found money by ____ tree.

7. They could also find money by ____ river.

8. This money was ____ hard, round, stone!

9. Small stones the size of ____ egg might buy ____ chicken.

10. Big stones, those too big to carry, might buy ____ elephant.

11. People once used ____ block of salt for money.

12. However, salt often melted in ____ rain.

13. ____ improvement came when people started to make metal money.

14. ____ early coin might have been made out of gold, silver, or copper.

15. Today, we use metal coins and paper to buy ____ item.

Extension: Have students do some research by reading 250 words from their reader, science, or social studies text and counting the number of times *a, an,* and *the* appear.

Name

Mechanics: Capitalizing
Proper Adjectives

Proper adjectives are formed from proper nouns. Proper adjectives refer to particular people, places, or things. Proper adjectives are always capitalized.

Italy   **I**talian people   Washington   **W**ashington newspaper

A. Underline the proper adjective in each sentence.

1. Think about all the European foods you have eaten.
2. Have you ever tasted Irish stew?
3. Hotdogs were made by German butchers.
4. My favorite dinner is Sicilian pizza.
5. America is also known for its foods, like Maine lobster.
6. Virginia ham is a great favorite for many holidays.
7. Let's not forget New England clam chowder.
8. More good foods can be found in the Southern states.
9. There are also wonderful Mexican foods.
10. Of all of these foods, my sister still likes Chinese food the best.

B. Write proper adjectives using the proper nouns in parentheses.

11. How much do you know about (America) _____ history?

12. A (Spain) _____ queen sent Columbus to find America.

13. (Italy) _____ explorers also found land in America.

14. People from (Europe) _____ and (Asia)

_____ countries came to live in America.

15. The early colonies were ruled by a (Britain) _____ king.

Macmillan LANGUAGE ARTS TODAY
Grade 4, Unit 9, Lesson 7, pages 304–305

Macmillan Publishing Company

Extension: Have the students use proper adjectives to write four sentences about their favorite foods. Have students illustrate their sentences with pictures from magazines or newspapers.

Name _____

Vocabulary Building:
Synonyms and Antonyms

Synonyms are words that have the same meaning or almost the same meaning.

Word	Synonyms
big	large, huge, great, massive, enormous

Antonyms are words that have opposite meanings.

Word	Antonyms
big	small, little, tiny, mini,

A. Write a synonym for each underlined word.

1. The cars that go by my house are very <u>loud</u>. _____

2. Our dog Ralph is not allowed to <u>dash</u> around outside. _____

3. All the traffic makes it too <u>risky</u> for Ralph. _____

4. The windows even <u>rattle</u> when a truck goes by. _____

5. I really <u>adore</u> my home. _____

6. The noise, however, does make me <u>annoyed</u>. _____

7. When that happens, I take a <u>lengthy</u> walk. _____

B. Write an antonym for each underlined word.

8. This morning I got up <u>late</u>. _____

9. Then I couldn't find my <u>beautiful</u> picture for art class. _____

10. That's when everything fell out of my <u>thick</u> book. _____

11. Next, I tripped over a basket of <u>wet</u> clothes. _____

12. I slipped on a towel and landed on the <u>hard</u> floor. _____

13. And that was just the <u>beginning</u> of my day! _____

Macmillan Publishing Company

Macmillan LANGUAGE ARTS TODAY
Grade 4, Unit 9, Lesson 8, pages 306–307

Extension: Have students work in pairs. Have one student choose a word and have his or her partner provide a synonym or an antonym for the word. Have students switch roles and repeat the activity.

Name _____

Grammar and Writing Connection: Choosing Vivid Adjectives

> **Vivid adjectives** add detail and color to your writing. They make your word picture very clear.
>
> My sister is special.
> My sister is brave. ⟵ more precise

A. Write a more vivid adjective for each underlined adjective.

1. One day there was a bad storm. _____

2. Sandra was going home by the large lake. _____

3. The water was rough. _____

4. The strong wind was breaking off tree branches. _____

5. Then my sister heard a loud cry. _____

6. She spotted a small boat. _____

7. A scared boy was inside. _____

8. My sister ran down the wet road to the boat house. _____

9. The nice lake guards sent a boat out for the boy. _____

10. The boy was happy to see help on the way. _____

B. Rewrite the sentences. Replace each underlined adjective with a more precise one. You may want to use a thesaurus.

11. Our trip to the local newspaper was enjoyable.

_____

12. A good guide took us through the plant.

_____

13. Working on a newspaper is a nice job.

_____

Extension: Ask students to look at advertisements in magazines or newspapers to find descriptions that include precise and vivid adjectives.

Macmillan Publishing Company

Name _____

Group Writing:
A Description

> The purpose of a description is to create a clear and vivid picture. The following help make a picture clear and vivid.
> - An **overall impression** is the general idea.
> - **Sensory details** tell more about how things look, sound, taste, feel, or smell.
> - **Details** are arranged in logical order.

A. Read this paragraph. Then follow the directions.

    The tour guide took us through the entrance of the castle. As we walked inside, we felt like we had gone through time and were now back in the 1500s. Because of the thick stone walls, the rooms and hallways felt cool and smelled damp. I was sorry that I had forgotten to bring a sweater. Candles flickered in the dark hallways. Then we entered the grand dining hall. We could almost see a roasted pig sitting in the middle of the huge wooden table.

1. Write the overall impression of this paragraph.

_____

_____

2. Write three sensory detail sentences that support the overall impression.

   a. _____

      _____

   b. _____

      _____

   c. _____

      _____

B. Based on what you know about castles, write two more sensory detail sentences that could be added to this paragraph. Use another sheet of paper.

Extension: Have students write two sensory details for a description of their school.

Name _____

Thinking and Writing:
Classifying Sensory Details

When you write a **description,** you must decide which sensory details are important to the overall impression of your description. You should include only the sensory details that support the overall impression.

Each of the writers named below is planning to write a description. Help each one to decide which details to include. Underline the detail that should <u>not</u> be included.

1. Lien's paragraph will describe a garage. She wants to create an overall impression of the mess inside the garage.
   - **a.** old car and bicycle tires
   - **b.** stacks of newspapers
   - **c.** a red car driving down the road
   - **d.** different sized empty boxes

2. Paul's paragraph will describe the inside of an airport. He wants to create an overall impression of noise and confusion.
   - **a.** crowded highways leading to the airport
   - **b.** announcements over the loud speaker of planes landing and taking off
   - **c.** long lines of people going through the security check
   - **d.** people pushing each other to get their luggage

3. Chico's paragraph will describe his bedroom. He wants to create an overall impression of his bedroom as a restful, comfortable place to be.
   - **a.** a large bed with soft blankets
   - **b.** a big, soft, easy chair
   - **c.** warm sunlight coming through the window
   - **d.** lawn chairs in the yard below

4. Andrew's paragraph will describe a video game store at the mall. He wants to give an overall impression of the noise and excitement in the store.
   - **a.** two or three teenagers at each video game
   - **b.** loud cheers when someone scores a point
   - **c.** the men's clothing store next door
   - **d.** bells and other sounds coming from the machines

Macmillan LANGUAGE ARTS TODAY
Grade 4, Unit 10, Lesson 2, pages 338–339

Macmillan Publishing Company

Extension: Have students choose a room or place and make a list of the sensory details that they would use to describe it to someone. Ask students to draw a picture of the place.

Name _____

Proofreading: Step 4

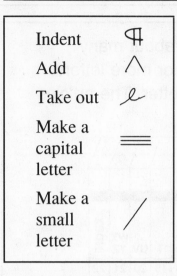

Indent	⁋
Add	∧
Take out	ℓ
Make a capital letter	≡
Make a small letter	/

Read the reporter's opening remarks about an important ice hockey game. See if the adjectives that compare two or more nouns are used correctly. Also see if adjectives that describe particular people, places, or things are capitalized.

A. Mark any changes or corrections you want to make with proofreading marks from the box.

Tonight the Chips meet the Slammers. This should be the more

exciting hockey game of the new england season. This game will tell

which team is the more talented in the northeastern region. The crowd

is the more enthusiastic I have ever seen. The Chips are most

experienced than the Slammers. The Chips are also most cautious

than the Slammers, however. Stay tuned for the results of this game!

B. Rewrite the reporter's paragraph on the lines below. Include the changes and corrections you marked above.

_____

_____

_____

_____

_____

_____

_____

Name _____

Writer's Resources:
The Encyclopedia

An **encyclopedia** is a set of books with information about many subjects. Each book, or volume, is labeled with one or more letters. Each volume includes subjects beginning with that letter. The articles are arranged alphabetically.

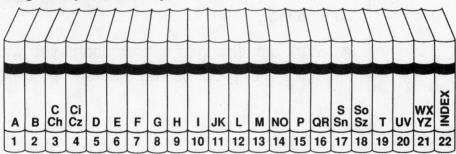

The last volume is an index of all subjects written about in the whole set of books.

Write the number of the encyclopedia volume that would have an article on each of the following subjects. Use the set of encyclopedias above.

1. fishing _____

2. kites _____

3. China _____

4. Pablo Picasso _____

5. snakes _____

6. the March of Dimes _____

7. Walt Disney _____

8. baseball _____

9. the use of robots in business _____

10. the discoveries of Marie Curie _____

11. hints for taking good photographs _____

12. pigeons that carry messages _____

13. meat-eating dinosaurs _____

Extension: Ask each student to think of three topics that he or she would like to learn more about. Then have each student find those topics in the encyclopedia.

Name _____

What Is a Pronoun?

> A **pronoun** is a word that takes the place of one or more nouns.
> Singular pronouns are **I, me, you, he, she, him, her,** and **it.**
> Plural pronouns are **we, us, they, them.**
>
> Betsy is my sister.　　Betsy and Lynn are my sisters.
> She is my sister.　　They are my sisters.

A. Underline the pronoun in each sentence. Write **S** if the pronoun is singular or **P** if the pronoun is plural.

1. "I have a tent," Betsy said. ____

2. "We should have sleeping bags," Lynn added. ____

3. "I have one sleeping bag," Wendy said. ____

4. "Good, it will come in handy," Lynn said. ____

5. "Mrs. Ryan might offer her sleeping bag," Wendy continued. ____

6. "Then we only need two more of them." ____

7. "Tim and Bob might lend me two sleeping bags," Lynn said. ____

8. "No," Betsy said, "they are out of town." ____

9. "Maybe two sleeping bags will be enough for us," Lynn said. ____

10. "I can sleep in the tent with blankets," Wendy added. ____

B. Underline each pronoun. Write the noun each pronoun takes the place of.

11. "I just read a book about lions," Joe said. _____

12. "They hunt at night," Joe explained. _____

13. "You would like this book about lions," Joe told Sue. _____

14. "We should do a report on lions," Joe said. _____

15. "It would be fun to work on," agreed Sue. _____

Extension: Have students choose four sentences from Part A, two with singular pronouns and two with plural pronouns. Ask students to rewrite the sentences by changing the singular pronouns to plural and the plural pronouns to singular.

Name _____

Subject Pronouns

> A **subject pronoun** is a pronoun that is used as the subject of a sentence. The singular subject pronouns are **I, you, she, he,** and **it.** The plural subject pronouns are **we, you,** and **they.**
>
> Brad joined a contest.   Chris and Lee joined, too.
> He joined a contest.   They joined, too.

A. Write the subject pronoun of each sentence.

1. You just won the first prize! _____

2. It is a week's trip to Disney World. _____

3. We will even supply the airplane tickets. _____

4. They will be waiting for you at the airport. _____

5. I hope that Disney World will be fun. _____

B. Read each pair of sentences. The second sentence in each pair is missing a pronoun. Write the pronoun on the blank.

6. Every spring Dad plants a garden. _____ enjoys gardening.

7. Of course, Amy and I help. _____ put the seeds into the ground.

8. Dad and Amy usually weed. _____ like the exercise.

9. Mom helps, too. _____ waters the garden.

10. Lettuce grows well in our garden. _____ tastes delicious in salads.

11. Fresh corn and peas are good. _____ taste very different from canned corn and peas.

12. Dad always plants too many beans. _____ planted too many again this year.

Extension: Have each student write two sentences using a singular subject pronoun and two sentences using a plural subject pronoun.

Macmillan Publishing Company

Name _____

Object Pronouns

> An **object pronoun** is a pronoun that may be used after an action verb in a sentence. The singular object pronouns are **me, you, him, her,** and **it**. The plural object pronouns are **us, you,** and **them**.
>
> The coach gave <u>Jason</u> a signal.   The coach called to <u>Bill and Jeff</u>.
> The coach gave <u>him</u> a signal.   The coach called to <u>them</u>.

A. Write the object pronoun of each sentence.

1. "Throw me the ball," Jason called out. _____

2. The catcher threw him the ball. _____

3. Jason caught it easily and tagged the runner. _____

4. Jason called the players together and told them the next play. _____

5. The coach will tell you the rest of the story. _____

B. Read each pair of sentences. Complete the second sentence with the correct pronoun in parentheses. Use the underlined word or words as clues.

6. Mom gets <u>*The Old Farmer's Almanac.*</u> She enjoys (her, it) _____ very much.

7. The almanac gives <u>forecasts</u> of the weather for the whole year. Mom reads (they, them) _____ all the time.

8. The almanac supplies <u>Mom</u> with other helpful information. For example, it gives (she, her) _____ a list of all the holidays.

9. Sometimes Mom shares information with <u>Dad</u>. She tells (him, he) _____ about a nice poem she read in the almanac.

10. One day Mom read <u>Dad and me</u> a funny story. She read (we, us) _____ the story from the almanac.

Extension: Have students write one more sentence using a singular object pronoun and one more sentence using a plural object pronoun for Part A. Have them underline the object pronoun in each sentence.

Name _____

Possessive Pronouns

> A **possessive pronoun** is a pronoun that shows who or what owns something. The singular possessive pronouns are **my, your, her, his,** and **its.** The plural possessive pronouns are **our, your,** and **their.**
>
> Paul has a blue pencil. <u>His</u> pencil is blue.
> <u>Paul</u> and <u>David</u> are brothers. <u>Their</u> pencils are both blue.

A. Read each sentence. Write the possessive pronoun.

1. "Is this your pencil?" Paul asked David. _____

2. "No, my pencil is on the desk," David answered. _____

3. "Pam lost her pencil this morning," David continued. _____

4. "Look, its point is broken," Paul said. _____

5. "Well, just add it to our collection of pencils to be sharpened!" David said. _____

B. Read each pair of sentences. Complete each sentence with the correct pronoun in parentheses. Use the underlined word or words as clues.

6. <u>We</u> took a tour of the *Morning Herald Newspaper* building.

   (Our, Their) _____ tour was very informative.

7. Do you know <u>Frank Bryan</u>?

   (He, His) _____ son Walter works at the *Herald.*

8. Walter works in the main offices of the <u>Herald.</u>

   (Its, His) _____ main offices are on Parker Street.

9. My <u>mother</u> once worked at the *Herald* also.

   (Their, Her) _____ job was to write stories.

Macmillan Publishing Company

Extension: Have students write four more sentences using the pronouns they did not choose in sentences 6-9.

Name _____

Using *I* and *me* Correctly

> **I** is used in the subject part of a sentence. **Me** is used after an action verb or words such as **in, into, with, by,** or **at.**
>
> I like sports.
> Sometimes running gives me leg cramps.

Complete each sentence with **I** or **me.**

1. _____ joined the school track team.

2. My brother gave _____ some helpful hints.

3. For example, now _____ know a lot about running shoes.

4. Speed-right running shoes are the best for _____ .

5. _____ couldn't run well when my feet hurt.

6. _____ often visit my grandmother after school.

7. She always asks _____ for a little help.

8. Once, _____ carried some things up to her attic for her.

9. Another time _____ painted her small table white.

10. During that time, she told _____ a story about the table.

11. One day she will give _____ the table.

12. _____ like doing these jobs for her.

13. Grandmother and _____ like to take long walks.

14. This activity gives _____ the opportunity to talk with Grandmother.

15. Afterwards _____ go home for supper.

Extension: Have students work in small groups. Have them take turns telling each other about their day using the words *I* and *me.*

Name _____

Mechanics: Pronoun Contractions

> A **contraction** is a word made up of two words. Use an **apostrophe** (') to stand for the letters that are left out in a contraction.
>
> | | | | | | | | |
> |---|---|---|---|---|---|---|---|
> | I am | = I'm | it is | = it's | we are | = we're |
> | you have | = you've | he had/would | = he'd | she is/has | = she's |
> | I will | = I'll | it will | = it'll | we will | = we'll |

A. Write the contraction for each underlined word.

1. <u>It is</u> five o'clock. _____

2. <u>She has</u> been late before. _____

3. <u>We are</u> usually on time. _____

4. <u>I will</u> call her soon. _____

5. <u>You are</u> never late. _____

B. Write the two words that make up each contraction. Then write a sentence that uses the contraction. Remember to add the apostrophe.

6. he's _____

_____

7. we've _____

_____

8. I'm _____

_____

9. you'd _____

_____

10. we'll _____

_____

Extension: Have students choose five contractions from the box to add sentences to Part A.

Name _____

Vocabulary Building:
Homophones and Homographs

Homophones are words that sound the same but have different spellings and meanings.

I have a <u>new</u> bicycle.   I <u>knew</u> the answer.

Homographs are words that are spelled the same but have different meanings. Some homographs also have different pronunciations.

I was <u>present</u> at school yesterday.   Here is a <u>present</u> for you.
I <u>present</u> you with this award.

A. Write the correct word in parentheses.

1. Have you finished the (hole, whole) job?   _____

2. Yes, but I accidentally cut a (hole, whole)
   in my jacket.   _____

3. I don't know (weather, whether) to take
   an umbrella.   _____

4. The (weather, whether) looks dark and gloomy.   _____

5. (Their, There) go the Hendersons.   _____

6. They are going to (their, there) summer home.   _____

B. Complete each sentence with a word from the box.

duck	object	pen

7. My _____ just ran out of ink.

8. If you _____, you won't get hit by the ball.

9. The strange _____ in the box is a piece of art.

10. Someone let the pigs out of their _____.

11. I _____ to the new rules.

12. Look at the cute _____ in the pond.

Extension: Ask students to use a dictionary to find three pairs of homphones and three pairs of homographs.

Macmillan Publishing Company

Name _____

Grammar and Writing Connection: Combining Sentences

If you combine two or more sentences, you may list several words in a **series.** Use **and** or **or** before the last word in a series. Words in a series are separated by commas.

SEPARATE: Beets are growing in his garden.
Peas are growing in his garden.
Beans are growing in his garden.

JOINED: Beets, peas, and beans are growing in his garden.

Combine these groups of sentences by joining words in a series.

1. Should Tony plant lettuce?
Should Tony plant squash?
Should Tony plant carrots?

_____

2. Tony weeded the garden.
Mom weeded the garden.
Dad weeded the garden.

_____

3. Bees flew around the garden.
Wasps flew around the garden.
Birds flew around the garden.

_____

4. Did Tony pick the corn?
Did Tony pick the squash?
Did Tony pick the peas?

_____

5. We put fresh lettuce in our salad.
We put fresh carrots in our salad.
We put fresh tomatoes in our salad.

_____

Extension: Have students write a list of things they would buy at a grocery store. Then, have them write five sentences using the items from the list in a series.

Macmillan Publishing Company

Name _____

Group Writing:
A Persuasive Paragraph

> In a **persuasive paragraph,** the writer tries to **convince an audience** to agree with the writer's opinion. The topic sentence usually states the opinion. Reasons that support the opinion follow, with the most important reasons given first. Facts should be included because they help persuade the audience that the opinion is sound.

A. Put an **X** next to each sentence that could be a topic sentence for a persuasive paragraph.

1. _____ When the planes are landing at the airport, they fly too low over the tops of the houses.

2. _____ The school day should be shortened to four hours.

3. _____ More turkeys are raised in California than in any other state.

4. _____ A giraffe can go without water longer than a camel can.

5. _____ Students who are ten years old should be able to get a work permit so they can earn extra money.

B. Read the topic sentence for a persuasive paragraph. Then underline each sentence that could be used to support the topic sentence.

6. Topic sentence: People shouldn't let their dogs run freely.
   a. Dogs can ruin people's flowers and shrubs.
   b. Dogs make better pets than cats do.
   c. Loose dogs could frighten people who are scared of dogs.
   d. Dogs should be fed only once a day.
   e. Dogs could upset other neighborhood pets who are tied on a leash.

7. Topic sentence: People should save some of the money they earn.
   a. They will be able to afford more goods and services.
   b. There will be money for a "rainy day."
   c. They should deposit their money in savings accounts with banks.
   d. They seldom will need to use credit cards to make a purchase.
   e. People can arrange to have a part of their salaries automatically placed in a savings account each week.

Extension: Have students find an example of a persuasive paragraph in the advertisements of a newspaper or magazine.

Name _____

Thinking and Writing:
Telling Fact from Opinion

A **fact** is a statement that can be proven or checked. An **opinion** is something that is believed. It cannot be proven or checked.

fact ⟶ There are fifteen children in gym class.

opinion ⟶ Most of them seem to be enjoying the activities.

A. Write **fact** if the statement is a fact or **opinion** if the statement is an opinion.

1. Exercise strengthens the heart muscles. _____

2. Gym class is a waste of time. _____

3. Students will feel better after they exercise. _____

4. Exercise burns off calories to help control weight. _____

5. Students feel foolish doing activities such as chasing a ball around a court. _____

6. Students should be able to pursue other interests during gym class time. _____

7. Some exercise is necessary for a healthy body. _____

8. Exercises that are too difficult can hurt muscles and cause pain. _____

B. Following is a topic sentence for a persuasive paragraph. Write one fact and one opinion to support the topic sentence.

Topic sentence: The best way to travel is by airplane.

9. **fact:** _____

10. **opinion:** _____

Macmillan Publishing Company

Extension: Have students look through magazines or newspapers to find two examples of a fact and two examples of an opinion.

Name _____

● Proofreading: Step 4

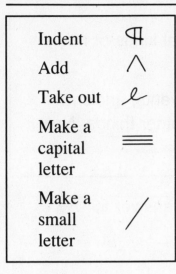

Indent	¶
Add	∧
Take out	ℓ
Make a capital letter	≡
Make a small letter	/

Read the following paragraph about plans for a surprise birthday party. Check to see if all the pronouns are used correctly. Also make sure that an apostrophe (') replaces the letter or letters left out of contractions.

A. Use the proofreading marks to mark any changes or corrections in the paragraph.

　　Mrs. Harmon will make the cake. Shell hide him in the closet. Nick said hed be home by two o'clock. Then hell probably go outside to shoot baskets. Jody and Harve will join he. Theyll ask to look at Harve's bike. Its fine, but Nick won't know that. When them finally come into the house, well yell, "Surprise!"

B. Write the paragraph on the lines below. Make the changes and corrections you marked above.

_____
_____
_____
_____
_____
_____
_____
_____

Writer's Resources: The Atlas and the Almanac

An **atlas** is a book of maps. It usually contains several kinds of maps for one area.

An **almanac** gives facts about populations, current events, ancient history, famous people, sports, elections, and many other things. New almanacs come out every year.

Write **atlas** or **almanac** to tell where you would find the answer to each question.

1. What are the ten most popular magazines in the United States? _____

2. What is the largest country in South America? _____

3. How far is Columbus, Ohio, from Cincinnati, Ohio? _____

4. What war started in 1914? _____

5. What was the lowest temperature in New York City last year? _____

6. What state is directly north of New Mexico? _____

7. What is the longitude and latitude of New Zealand? _____

8. In what state was James Monroe, the fifth President of the United States, born? _____

9. What is the largest city near Macon, Georgia? _____

10. What animals might soon become extinct? _____

11. What football team won the Super Bowl in 1987? _____

12. What large lake is near West Palm Beach, Florida? _____

13. Iceland is closest to what continent? _____

14. What is the highest mountain in the world? _____

Extension: Have students use an atlas and an almanac to answer some of the questions on this page.

Macmillan Publishing Company

Name _____

What Is an Adverb?

An **adverb** is a word that tells more about a verb.

An adverb may tell **how** an action takes place.
  We <u>secretly</u> planned a birthday party for my mother.

An adverb may tell **when** an action takes place.
  We will have the party <u>today</u>.

An adverb may tell **where** an action takes place.
  We will have the party <u>here</u>.

A. Underline the adverb in each sentence. Write whether the adverb tells **how, when,** or **where.**

1. My mother's birthday is tomorrow. _____

2. I carefully chose her present. _____

3. I wrapped it nicely. _____

4. I hid it here. _____

5. It is well hidden. _____

6. She will never find it. _____

7. I always give her a card. _____

B. Complete each sentence with an adverb from the box.

almost	completely	down	never	soon
already	daily	gladly	now	totally

8. You _____ missed Mom's party.

9. Everyone is here _____.

10. Enjoy yourself _____.

11. Mom will open her presents _____.

Extension: Have students draw an arrow from each adverb to the verb it tells more about in sentences 1–7.

Name _____

More About Adverbs

> An **adverb** is a word that tells more about a verb. It tells **where, when,** and **how.**
>
> An adverb can be put at the beginning of a sentence, before or after the verb, or at the end of a sentence. If you use an adverb to begin a sentence, place a comma after it.
>
> <u>Suddenly</u>, something flew through the window.
> Something <u>suddenly</u> flew through the window.
> Something flew <u>suddenly</u> through the window.
> Something flew through the window <u>suddenly</u>.

A. Underline each adverb. Then write whether the adverb tells **where, when,** or **how.**

1. Come here and read this article about the heart. _____

2. The writer thoroughly researched her subject. _____

3. Your heart is pumping blood constantly. _____

4. Yearly, your heart beats more than 36 million times. _____

5. Your heart beats faster when you exercise. _____

6. Let's go outside and play ball. _____

7. My heart is pounding quickly. _____

8. I feel better already. _____

B. Underline the correct word in parentheses.

9. (Actual, Actually), your heart doesn't look like a valentine.
10. Doctors can listen (closely, close) to the sound of your heart.
11. Small valves (constantly, constant) regulate the flow of blood.
12. These valves must work (correct, correctly).
13. (Quickly, Quick), doctors can tell if something is wrong.

Extension: Have students write six sentences about their class or school. Have students write two sentences using adverbs that tell where, two sentences using adverbs that tell when, and two sentences using adverbs that tell how.

Name

Using Adverbs to Compare

Add **er** to compare two actions.

Lee is quicker than Jo.

Add **est** to compare more than two actions.

Lee is the quickest person on the team.

Use **more** and **most** to form comparisons with adverbs ending in **ly** and with longer adverbs. Use **more** to compare two actions.

Jo ran more slowly than Lee.

Use **most** to compare more than two actions.

Of everyone on the team, Tim ran the most slowly.

Decide whether to use **er, est, more,** or **most** to make the correct form of the adverb in parentheses. Write the sentence correctly.

1. Who can run (fast), your horse Lightning or my horse Thunder?

_____

2. I know that Lightning can jump (high) than Thunder.

_____

3. Of all the horses in the stable, Lightning runs (quickly).

_____

4. However, Thunder works (hard) than Lightning.

_____

5. Sometimes Lightning stops (abruptly) than Thunder.

_____

6. Lightning will get you to the barn (soon) than Thunder.

_____

7. Of all the horses I have ever ridden, Thunder gallops (easily).

Extension: Have students take turns comparing two animals by using adverbs with the *er* and *est* endings, as well as adverbs with the words *more* and *most.*

Macmillan Publishing Company

Name _____

Using *good* and *well* Correctly

Use the adjective **good** to describe nouns.

The juice tastes good.

It was made from good oranges.

Use the adverb **well** to tell more about verbs.

You squeezed the oranges well.

A. Write the correct word in parentheses.

1. Oranges are (good, well) for your health.   _____

2. A (good, well) vitamin in oranges is vitamin C.   _____

3. Vitamins make your body work (good, well).   _____

4. The article about vitamins in this magazine was
   (good, well).   _____

5. The article was written (good, well).   _____

B. Complete each sentence with the word **good** or **well.**

6. That movie last night was really _____.

7. The special effects were especially _____.

8. The monster from outer space walked so _____.

9. It moved its eyes _____, too.

10. I have also seen other _____ movies lately.

11. Most movies today are made _____.

12. The acting is usually _____.

13. The stories are told _____.

14. A monster movie must have a _____ make-up artist.

15. The prices at the theater near my house are _____.

Extension: Have students draw an arrow from *good* or *well* to the noun or verb it tells about.

Macmillan Publishing Company

Name _____

Negatives

> **Negatives** are words that make a sentence mean "no." Common negatives are **no, none, no one, nowhere, not, never, nobody,** and **nothing.** Contractions with **n't** are also negatives because the contraction **n't** stands for **not.**
>
> Use only one negative in a sentence. If you have two negatives, change one to a positive without changing the meaning of the sentence.
>
> Nobody saw ~~nothing~~.
> Nobody saw anything.
> The people saw nothing.

Change the negative word in parentheses to a positive word. Rewrite each sentence correctly.

1. I (haven't) never used this camera before.

_____

2. I don't see (no) place for film.

_____

3. I can't see (nobody) through this lens.

_____

4. Oops! I hadn't (never) taken off the lens cap.

_____

5. Never take pictures in (no) hurry.

_____

6. I don't want to take pictures of (no one).

_____

7. My sister has taken six pictures, but I haven't taken (none) yet.

_____

Macmillan Publishing Company

Extension: Have students write **N** above each negative word in sentences 1-7.

Name _____

Mechanics: Punctuating Titles

- Capitalize the first, last, and all important words in a title.

    ***B**eauty and the **B**east*

- Underline titles of books, newspapers, and magazines.

    <u>The Wind in the Willows</u>   <u>The New York TImes</u>   <u>Newsweek</u>

- Use quotation marks to punctuate titles of articles, stories, songs, and poems.

    "The Mitten"   "The Hokey-Pokey"   "Holding Hands"

Rewrite each sentence. Capitalize each title correctly and use underlining or quotation marks.

1. When my class went to the library, I checked out the fun book of facts.

   _____

2. For her book report, Cora chose great inventions of the past.

   _____

3. I noticed that Otis was reading the magazine highlights for children.

   _____

4. Because Brad was from Chicago, he was looking at the chicago tribune.

   _____

5. Pepe was looking for the song Bingo.

   _____

6. I saw Nina carrying a book that included the poem storm at night.

   _____

Extension: Have students think of imaginary titles. Have them write their titles and punctuate them correctly.

Name _____

Vocabulary Building:
Borrowed Words

Borrowed words are words from other languages that became part of our language with time.

glen (Scottish)	octopus (Greek)	skipper (Dutch)
kangaroo (Australian)	poncho (Spanish)	squash (Native American)
kindergarten (German)	senate (Latin)	taco (Mexican/American)
liberty (French)	shamrock (Irish)	violin (Italian)

A dictionary often will tell you from which language a borrowed word comes.

Complete each sentence with a word from the box. If a word is unfamiliar, look up its meaning in a dictionary.

1. The _____ will meet to discuss important matters.

2. Did you see the baby _____ riding in its mother's pouch?

3. The _____ is a difficult instrument to learn to play.

4. The _____ of this ship is Captain Morrison.

5. If you get cold, put on this _____ .

6. I learned to write my name in _____ .

7. The _____ is the emblem of Ireland.

8. The last words of the "Pledge of Allegiance" are "with _____ and justice for all."

9. I enjoy eating fresh _____ every summer.

10. A _____ is a small and lonely valley.

11. The _____ we had for lunch at the Mexican restaurant was delicious.

12. The _____ lived in a deep, dark part of the ocean.

Extension: Ask students to use the dictionary to find three more examples of borrowed words. Have them tell which countries the words came from.

Name

Grammar and Writing Connection:
Combining Sentences

When sentences have similar ideas, you can often combine them by joining words and phrases that tell **how, where,** or **when.**

SEPARATE: Ken flew his paper airplane smoothly. (tells **how**)
Ken flew his paper airplane high. (tells **where**)
Ken flew his paper airplane often. (tells **when**)
JOINED: Ken flew his paper airplane smoothly, high, and often.

Combine these groups of sentences by joining words that tell **how, where,** or **when.**

1. Ken made his airplane slowly. Ken made it carefully.

_____

2. He worked quietly. He worked in the basement.

_____

3. Ken drew different designs. Ken drew them again and again.

_____

4. One night Ken worked late. He worked in his room.

_____

5. He made the best design. He made it near midnight.

_____

6. "I did it!" he shouted loudly. "I did it!" he shouted with excitement.

_____

Extension: Have students write pairs of sentences about something they have made or would like to make. Have them combine the sentences by using joining words that tell *how, where,* or *when.*

Macmillan Publishing Company

Name

Group Writing:
A Research Report

The **purpose** of a research report is to give information to an **audience** about a specific topic.

- **Notetaking** helps you remember what you have read.
- An **outline** helps you to organize a report.

Title

I. Main idea ──────────────────→ will be a paragraph
  A. Detail that supports the main idea ──────→ subtopic
  B. Detail that supports the main idea ──────→ subtopic

Bears

I. Different kinds of bears
  A. Black bears
  B. Polar bears

A research report should be organized in a logical manner.

Read the following paragraph and write an outline for it.

The Great Wall of China is almost 4,000 miles long. It is the longest structure that has ever been built. It crosses northern China from the east coast to the central part of China. The Great Wall is about 25 feet high. It's width ranges from 25 feet at the base to 15 feet at the top. The Chinese built this long, high wall to protect themselves against their enemies.

_____

_____

_____

_____

_____

Macmillan Publishing Company

Extension: Ask students to add another detail sentence to the outline on the Great Wall of China.

Name

Thinking and Writing: Summarizing

A **summary** tells the main idea and the most important facts of a longer piece of writing. When you summarize information, keep your audience and purpose in mind. Choose only those details that are the most important.

Imagine that you are a journalist for your school paper. Write a three-sentence summary of this report for your schoolmates.

SCHOOL NEWS

September 19, 1990. The School Board met last night to discuss the need for a gym at the Parker Elementary School. Students at the school can play various group sports only when the weather allows them to go outside. On rainy days and during the cold winter, the students must stay inside the small, old gym. In this gym, their activities are limited. Jonathan Marshall, a School Board member, reminded the group that healthy bodies learn better. He went on to say that he thinks the students at Parker are being deprived of an important part of their education. At the end of the meeting, the School Board voted to look into the matter. Carrie Thompson volunteered to find out the cost of a new gym by the next meeting.

Extension: Have students write a short summary of the book or article that they have most recently read and enjoyed.

Macmillan Publishing Company

● Proofreading: Step 4

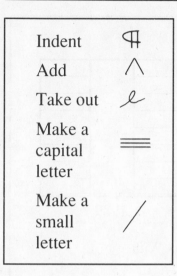

Indent	¶
Add	∧
Take out	ℓ
Make a capital letter	≡
Make a small letter	/

Read the paragraph about a young girl cleaning her room. Make sure that adverbs are spelled and used correctly. Also make sure that the book titles are written correctly.

A. Mark changes and corrections in the paragraph with proofreading marks from the box.

Kristie started to clean her room. First, she slow dusted the furniture. Then, she careful swept the floor. The dirt came up very easy. Next, she rapid scrubbed the paint. After that, she very neat hung some clean curtains. Finally, she loving wiped the covers of her two favorite books: *The practical princess And Other Stories* and *James and the giant Peach.*

B. Write the paragraph on the lines below. Include the changes and corrections you marked above.

_____

_____

_____

_____

_____

_____

_____

Writer's Resources: Graphs, Tables, and Maps

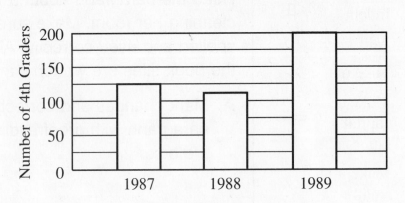

Graphs and **tables** are good ways of showing information about numbers.

Fourth-Grade Students With City Library Cards

A **table** can help you see and compare information. This table compares the number of fourth graders at different schools who have a library card for the city library.

School	Boys	Girls	Total
Jackson Elementary	12	18	30
Richmond Elementary	15	20	35
Kennedy Elementary	22	18	40

Maps also give facts. They show where things are and how far one place is from another.

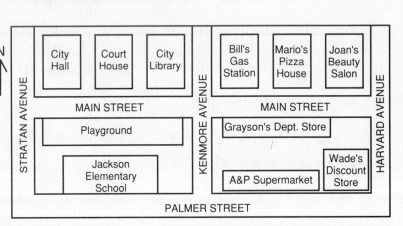

Use the graph, table, and map to answer the following questions.

1. In what year did the most fourth graders have city library cards? _____

2. Which school has the most fourth graders with city library cards? _____

3. If you went to Jackson Elementary School, would you go north or south to get to the city library? _____

Extension: Ask students to find examples of graphs, tables, and maps in their textbooks.

Macmillan Publishing Company